B

The UMAP Expository Monograph Series

Spatial Models of Election Competition
Steven J. Brams, *New York University*

Elements of the Theory of Generalized Inverses for Matrices
Randall E. Cline, *University of Tennessee*

Introduction to Population Modeling
James C. Frauenthal, *SUNY at Stony Brook*

Conditional Independence in Applied Probability
Paul E. Pfeiffer, *Rice University*

Topics in the Theory of Voting
Philip D. Straffin, Jr., *Beloit College*

The **UMAP** Expository Monograph Series

Topics in the Theory of Voting

Philip D. Straffin, Jr.

BIRKHÄUSER

BOSTON • BASEL • STUTTGART

Author

Philip D. Straffin, Jr.
Department of Mathematics
Beloit College
Beloit, Wisconsin 53511

Library of Congress Cataloging in Publication Data

Straffin, Philip D
    Topics in the theory of voting.

    (UMAP monograph)
    Includes bibliographical references and index.
    1. Voting. I. Title. II. Series.
JF1001.S77   324.9   80-23004
ISBN 3-7643-3017-1

CIP-Kurztitelaufnahme der Deutschen Bibliothek

Straffin, Philip D.:
Topics in the theory of voting / Philip D.
Straffin. - Boston, Basel, Stuttgart :
Birkhäuser, 1980.
    (umap)
    ISBN 3-7643-3017-1

This material was prepared with the partial support of
National Science Foundation Grant No. SED76-19615 A02.
Recommendations expressed are those of the author and do
not necessarily reflect the views of the NSF or the copyright
holder.

    Education Development Center, Inc. 1980
    ISBN 3-7643-3017-1
    Printed in USA

TABLE OF CONTENTS

Introduction

Voting occupies a central place in democratic theory
and practice: it is the process by which a society con-
sisting of individuals with disparate preferences decides
on one course of action. Yet voting is not a simple process, and even the earliest analytical work on the theory
of voting, by Jean-Charles de Borda and the Marquis de
Condorcet in the late eighteenth century, quickly revealed
that seemingly straightforward voting methods could hide
surprising logical subtleties. In the nineteenth century
these subtleties were further explored by the mathematician
C.L. Dodgson, whose appreciation of paradox is also evident
in his literary work under the pseudonym of Lewis Carroll.
However, the flowering of the analytical theory of voting
is a development of this century, beginning in the 1950's
with a series of influential works by Kenneth Arrow, Lloyd
Shapley and Martin Shubik, Duncan Black, and Robin
Farquharson. In the last twenty-five years, political
scientists, economists and mathematicians have built upon
these foundations an impressive body of ideas known as
social choice theory, or the theory of public choice. My
goal in this monograph is to explore some aspects of this
theory which appeal to my aesthetic sense as a mathematician, and which also have the potential to be useful in the
practical design of decision making procedures.

Chapter One deals with the problem of measuring <u>power</u>
in a voting body which must make a series of yes-or-no
decisions. In the design of such a body, many different
interests may have to be represented, possibly to varying
degrees. One way to do this is to assign representatives
of different interests different numbers of votes. Alter-
natively, in a one-person-one-vote body, voting blocs may

emerge which effectively give different interests different numbers of votes. To study the equity of such a body, we need a way to measure the effective voting power of different interests, and analysis reveals that the relationship of power to number of votes is a subtle one. The chapter develops a measure of voting power due to Shapley and Shubik, and applies it not only to weighted voting bodies, but to voting bodies with committees, and to decision-making procedures which involve two or more voting bodies.

Chapter Two discusses voting methods which can be used when decisions must be made among more than two alternatives. In such a case, "parliamentary procedures" can reduce the multi-alternative choice to a sequence of yes-or-no choices, but such a reduction is subject to a number of logical problems. The chapter presents eight other common voting methods, including plurality voting, elimination procedures, the Borda count, and various "Condorcet voting methods." These methods are evaluated according to a collection of reasonable criteria (one might think of them as axioms) which an ideal voting method might satisfy. Although no method is uniquely best, some methods do appear to be superior to others.

Chapter Three discusses two recent approaches to allowing voters to record the <u>intensity</u> of their preferences over a collection of alternatives. One very simple method is <u>approval voting</u>, which allows voters to vote for as many alternatives as they "approve of." An optimal strategy under such a system, at least in ignorance of how other voters feel, is to vote for those alternatives which are above average, according to your preference intensities. A second method of obtaining voter intensities is to allow voters to place numerical bids on alternatives. Here the main problem is how to encourage honesty in the placing of bids, and the chapter discusses a very recently developed process which does this. This "preference revealing process" is closely connected to both auctioning by sealed bids, and the free-rider problem in welfare economics.

I should say a word about the role of mathematics in this monograph. The mathematical prerequisites are minimal--some knowledge of permutations and combinations and a bit of algebra in Chapter One, and only the ability to follow a logical argument in Chapters Two and Three. I believe these ideas should be interesting to social scientists as well as mathematicians, and I have tried to make them accessible to as large an audience as possible. However, if there are no formulas in Chapters Two and Three, I think that there is much which is recognizable as a mathematical way of thinking. In particular, a mathematician should feel very at home with the axiom-counterexample method of Chapter Two. In many areas of social science, it may be that mathematics can contribute more by its method of thought than by the application of any specific mathematical technique.

It is possible, of course, to treat all of the subjects in the monograph using more formal mathematical techniques, and much of the research literature does this. For the reader with more mathematical background, I would recommend doing the problems at the end of each chapter, and then following the bibliographic notes to more advanced work in the references. I hope that all readers will find some of the problems interesting, and some of the references worth pursuing. Solutions for most of the problems appear at the end of the monograph.

Some of the examples in the text involve decision making in an environmental context. This reflects the historical genesis of the monograph. Most of it was written while I was visiting in the Department of Environmental Engineering Sciences at the University of Florida, on a Rockefeller Foundation Environmental Fellowship. In dealing with environmental problems, it has become increasingly evident that technical engineering knowledge has to be supplemented by a good deal of flexibility in soliciting and using information about public preferences and values. Hence environmental engineers have an interest in the recent work in social choice theory. Dr. James Heaney and the students in his seminar on "Political Analysis" at the University of Florida were the critical first audience for much of the material in this monograph, and made many suggestions for its improvement. An earlier version of the monograph, under the title Introduction to Social Choice Theory for Environmental Decision Making, was published by the American Society of Civil Engineers as Technical Memorandum #36 in the Urban Water Resources Research Program. I am grateful to the ASCE and to the series editor Murray McPherson for encouraging me to make the material available to a wider audience.

I also owe thanks to a number of other people who read and criticized part or all of the manuscript at various stages--Steven Brams, Peter Fishburn, Jerry Gustafson, Samuel Merrill, Kay Strangman, Nicholas Tideman, Robert Thrall, and Robert Weber--and to the staff at UMAP for their efficiency and cooperation.

Philip D. Straffin Jr.
Beloit, Wisconsin
March, 1980

1 Power in Voting Bodies

1.1 The Shapley-Shubik Index of Voting Power

Social decisions are made by a variety of legislative bodies and elected or appointed commissions in which many different interests are represented to varying degrees. In analyzing or designing such bodies, a fundamental question which must be addressed is: "How much power do certain individuals or interests have in this body?" For instance, if we can answer this analytic question, we are at least in a position to consider the associated ethical question: "Is this amount of power commensurate with the power that those individuals or interests ought to have?".

Of course, the word "power" as it is used in these questions is a highly ambiguous term. There are many kinds of power, and some of them, such as "persuasive power," are clearly unquantifiable. What analysts have been able to quantify is a very abstract form of voting power, which is, roughly, the chance that a given individual's vote, or the bloc of votes controlled by an interest group, will be crucial to the decision voted by the body. In this chapter we will describe the most well known measure of voting power, due to Shapley and Shubik [12], and demonstrate several possible uses for it. Clearly, a voting power measure will tell us only a little about a voting body. Interestingly, though, the little it can tell us is just at the right level of abstraction to be useful to those who must design a voting body. In addition, the Shapley-Shubik measure of voting power is based on a model of coalition formation which may make it applicable even to a body where few formal votes are taken at all.

To illustrate the reasoning behind Shapley and Shubik's voting power measure, consider a four-person com-

1

mittee in which each member has one vote. Call the members
of the committee A, B, C and D, and let A be the chairman.
The committee is faced with a series of motions or "bills,"
on each of which the members will vote "yes" or "no."
Since a 2-2 voting deadlock is possible, it is agreed that
the chairman A will be empowered to break ties. This tie-
breaking rule obviously gives A more voting power than the
other committee members. How much more?

Shapley and Shubik consider the process of building
coalitional support for a particular bill. The bill might
be most enthusiastically supported by, say, member B, second most enthusiastically by D, next most by A, and least
by C. Thus B would be first to join a coalition in support
of the bill, followed by D. At this point the bill would
still lose, and in fact it will be able to win only if the
coalition can gain the suport of the next most enthusiastic
member A. Gaining A's support may require considerable
modification of the original bill, so that member A has
considerable say over the form in which the bill will pass,
if it passes. A has the crucial power in this situation.

In an abstract setting, we would not have _a priori_
knowledge about possible orders of coalition formation.
Shapley and Shubik hence propose that to measure abstract
voting power, we should consider all orders equally likely.
For each order, one member will be _pivotal_ in the sense
that A was above: the losing coalition will become winning
precisely when that member joins it. The pivotal member
holds the power. Hence, as our measure of a member's voting power we use the probability that that member will be
pivotal, assuming that all orders of coalition formation
are equally likely.

For our four-person example, there are $4! = 4 \cdot 3 \cdot 2 \cdot 1 =$
24 possible orders. The chairman A is pivotal in 12 of the
24 orders, while each of the other members is pivotal in
only 4 of the orders. I have underlined the pivotal member
in each order:

ABCD	ADBC	BCAD	CABD	CDAB	DBAC
ABDC	ADCB	BCDA	CADB	CDBA	DBCA
ACBD	BACD	BDAC	CBAD	DABC	DCAB
ACDB	BADC	BDCA	CBDA	DACB	DCBA

The _Shapley-Shubik power indices_ of the members are thus 12
out of 24 for A, 4 out of 24 for B, etc.:

$$(12/24, 4/24, 4/24, 4/24) \text{ or } (1/2, 1/6, 1/6, 1/6).$$
$$\quad A \qquad B \qquad C \qquad D \qquad\quad A \qquad B \qquad C \qquad D$$

The chairman's tie-breaking ability has given him _three
times_ as much power as each of the other committee members.
It is this kind of non-intuitive result which makes the

Shapley-Shubik index a useful analytical tool. We would only design this kind of voting rule for a committee if we were willing to give the chairman that much power. In the remaining sections of this chapter, we will see other uses of the Shapley-Shubik index.

Although Shapley and Shubik presented their power index in terms of the specific model of coalition formation given above, it is remarkable that many other seemingly different approaches to voting power lead to exactly the same index. For instance, Shapley and Shubik pointed out in [12] that if instead of passing power we consider blocking power, i.e., coalitions forming to defeat a bill, a model analogous to that above will lead us exactly to the Shapley-Shubik index. (This follows immediately from the fact that a member who is a passing pivot in an order will be a blocking pivot in the reverse order.) The index measures blocking power as well as passing power.

It is also possible to derive the Shapley-Shubik index from a voting model which makes no mention of coalition formation at all. Suppose that each bill which comes before our voting body has some a priori "acceptability level" p ($0 \leq p \leq 1$), which is the probability that any given member of the body will vote for it. The p for an individual member on some bills will be low, and on other bills will be high. Assume that any value of p between 0 and 1 is equally likely. Now, to measure the voting power of a member we ask: "What fraction of the time will his vote be crucial to the outcome, in the sense that changing his vote would change the outcome?" It is proved in [15] that the answer to this question, under the "acceptability level" assumption, is precisely equal to that member's Shapley-Shubik index.*

The fact that the Shapley-Shubik index appears at the end of so many disparate chains of reasoning is strong evidence that it is a natural measure of voting power. Since its appearance in 1954, it has been widely accepted and applied by political scientists. The bibliographic notes at the end of this chapter give references to discussions of the Shapley-Shubik index, and to its only major competitor, another power index due to John Banzhaf [1].

---

*The Shapley-Shubik index can also be justified as the specialization to voting games of the classical Shapley value, a well-known solution concept from the mathematical theory of n-person cooperative games. As such, it can be characterized as the only measure of voting power which satisfies a certain collection of simple axioms. The axiomatic approach to the Shapley value is discussed critically in Chapter 11 of [9]. The result of specializing the axioms to voting games is reviewed in Section 3.1 of [13].

1.2 Weighted Voting Bodies

In some voting situations it may be reasonable to weight one individual's vote more than another's. In many county governments in New York State, for instance, each town has one representative but the votes of representatives from larger towns are weighted more heavily. In the Council of Ministers of the European Community, the representatives of France, Germany, Italy and England have more voting weight than the representatives from Belgium, the Netherlands, Denmark, Ireland and Luxembourg. Corporate stockholders' votes are weighted by the amount of stock they own. In the German Genossenschaften (river basin water quality management agencies) voting weight is often apportioned among industries and muncipalities according to the amount of pollution each contributes. (See [7] for an analysis of this seemingly perverse voting system.)

Formally, a weighted voting body can be represented by a symbol

$$[q \; ; \; w_1, \; w_2, \; \ldots, \; w_n].$$

Here, w_1 through w_n are the voting weights (numbers of votes) of the n members of the body, and q is the "quota" of votes necessary to pass a motion. (We require that q be larger than $(w_1 + \ldots + w_n)/2$.) For example, the weightings of the six members of the Council of Ministers of the European Economic Community as it was in 1958 could be represented by the symbol

$$[12 \; ; \; 4, \; 4, \; 4, \; 2, \; 2, \; 1].$$
$$ F \quad G \quad I \quad B \quad N \quad L$$

France, Germany and Italy had four votes each, Belgium and the Netherlands two votes each, and Luxembourg a single vote, with 12 of the 17 votes being necessary to pass a motion. (These figures are from [3], p. 184.)

Shapley-Shubik power analysis can reveal surprising properties of weighted voting bodies. For instance, let us consider the 1958 European Economic Community. The theory of permutations tells us that there are $6!/(3!2!1!) = 60$ distinct orders in which we can arrange the numbers 4, 4, 4, 2, 2, 1. Of these 60 orders, it turns out that a "4" occupies the pivotal position in 42 orders, a "2" occupies the pivotal position in 18 orders, and the "1" never occupies the pivotal position. The Shapley-Shubik indices for the members were

$$(14/60, \; 14/60, \; 14/60, \; 9/60, \; 9/60, \; 0).$$
$$ F \qquad G \qquad I \qquad B \qquad N \qquad L$$

4

Thus, the voting power of the members was definitely <u>not</u> in proportion to their numbers of votes:

	Percentage of Votes	Percentage of Power
France, Germany or Italy	23.5%	23.3%
Belgium or Netherlands	11.8%	15.0%
Luxembourg	5.9%	0.0%

Belgium and the Netherlands had more power than their number of votes would indicate, and Luxembourg had no power at all in this voting body.

It is easy to see why Luxembourg has no power: it can never be pivotal because it can never change a losing coalition into a winning coalition. For it to do so, there would have to be some coalition not including Luxembourg with exactly 11 votes, but all coalitions not including Luxembourg have an even number of votes. Since any coalition which would lose without Luxembourg would also lose with Luxembourg, no coalition cares whether it includes Luxembourg or not. In the language of the theory of "voting games," Luxembourg is a "dummy." Analysis using the Shapley-Shubik power index can reveal the presence of dummies--surely an inequitable feature in a voting body.

Even if there are no dummies, the distribution of power may be much different than the distribution of votes. Consider for example:

$$[5 \; ; \; 2, \; 2, \; 1, \; 1] \; .$$
$$A \quad B \quad C \quad D$$

There are six possible orders:

2211   2121   2112   1221   1212   1122,

and a "2" pivots in five of them. The power indices are:

$$(5/12, \; 5/12, \; 1/12, \; 1/12).$$

A and B have only twice the number of votes of C and D, but five times the amount of power. If we need to design a weighted voting body, we can use the Shapley-Shubik index to avoid such non-obvious inequities in the distribution of power. For county governments in New York, the courts have ruled that any proposed weighted voting scheme must be accompanied by a power analysis, and that the proportion of power of a representative should not differ from the proportion of the population he represents by more than about 7%. (See [5] and [6] for details.)

Table 1.1 lists the Shapley-Shubik power indices for all <u>structurally distinct</u> weighted voting bodies with four or fewer voters. By "structurally distinct" I mean the following. Consider the weighted voting body

5

$$[6 \; ; \; 4, \; 3, \; 2, \; 1],$$
$$\text{A} \quad \text{B} \quad \text{C} \quad \text{D}$$

which is not in the list. The <u>winning coalitions</u> in this body are AB, AC, BCD and all coalitions which include one of these (ABC, ABD, ACD and ABCD). AB, AC, and BCD are called the <u>minimal winning coalitions</u> of the voting body. Any voting body which has these same minimal winning coalitions will have the same pivotal members for all orderings and hence the same distribution of power. We say two voting bodies with the same minimal winning coalitions are <u>structurally equivalent</u>. For instance, any four-person voting body with a dummy is structurally equivalent to a three person voting body. Looking down the list of combinations in Table 1.1 for minimal winning coalitions AB, AC and BCD, we see that [6; 4, 3, 2, 1] would be structurally equivalent to [5; 3, 2, 2, 1], and hence has Shapley-Shubik indices of (5/12, 3/12, 3/12, 1/12).

Finally, notice that a voting rule which does not explicitly mention voting weights may still be structurally equivalent to weighted voting. For instance, in our first example of a four-person committee with a tie-breaking chairman (page 2) the minimal winning coalitions are AB, AC, AD and BCD. From Table 1.1 we see that this voting body is structurally equivalent to the <u>weighted</u> voting body [3; 2, 1, 1, 1].

TABLE 1.1

SHAPLEY-SHUBIK INDICES OF WEIGHTED VOTING
BODIES WITH FOUR OR FEWER VOTERS

Minimal Winning Coalitions	Sample Weighted Voting Body	Shapley-Shubik Indices
A	[1; 1]	(1)
AB	[2; 1 , 1]	(1/2, 1/2)
AB, AC, BC	[2; 1, 1, 1]	(1/3, 1/3, 1/3)
ABC	[3; 1, 1, 1]	(1/3, 1/3, 1/3)
AB, AC	[3; 2, 1, 1]	(4/6, 1/6, 1/6)
ABC, ABD, ACD, BCD	[3; 1, 1, 1, 1]	(1/4, 1/4, 1/4, 1/4)
ABCD	[4; 1, 1, 1, 1]	(1/4, 1/4, 1/4, 1/4)
AB, AC, AD, BCD	[3; 2, 1, 1, 1]	(3/6, 1/6, 1/6, 1/6)
ABC, ABD, ACD	[4; 2, 1, 1, 1]	(3/6, 1/6, 1/6, 1/6)
AB, AC, AD	[4; 3, 1, 1, 1]	(9/12, 1/12, 1/12, 1/12)
AB, ACD, BCD	[4; 2, 2, 1, 1]	(2/6, 2/6, 1/6, 1/6)
ABC, ABD	[5; 2, 1, 1, 1]	(5/12, 5/12, 1/12, 1/12)
AB, ACD	[5; 3, 2, 1, 1]	(7/12, 3/12, 1/12, 1/12)
AB, AC, BCD	[5; 3, 2, 2, 1]	(5/12, 3/12, 3/12, 1/12)

1.3 The Power of Voting Blocs

Even in voting bodies where every member casts only a single vote, some members with common interests may vote together--they may form a voting _bloc_. If this happens, it will affect the distribution of power in the voting body. In fact, one can analyze a voting body with blocs as though it were a weighted voting body. For instance, in a seven person committee that is voting by majority rule, suppose that three voters form a voting bloc. The result can be thought of as the weighted voting body [4; 3, 1, 1, 1, 1] which would have power indices (6/10, 1/10, 1/10, 1/10, 1/10). The three-person bloc thus has 60% of the power. If four voters form a bloc, the result is [4; 4, 1, 1, 1] in which the bloc has _all_ the power and the other three members are dummies.

As this example makes clear, a single voting bloc in an otherwise heterogeneous voting body can have a dispro- portionate amount of power. For an example, consider the North Central Florida Regional Planning Council. North Central Florida is largely rural and the only major city is the university city of Gainesville, which contains about 22% of the population of the planning area. There are 36 members on the planning council, representing both counties and municipalities. Gainesville is represented directly by 8 representatives, and indirectly by another 5 representa- tives from Alachua County who reside in Gainesville. It thus has as many as 13/36 = 36% of the votes on the coun- cil. No other county or municipality has more than two representatives. Suppose that, at least on some issues, all 13 council representatives from Gainesville voted as a bloc. We could represent the result as a weighted voting body

$$[19; \underset{G}{13}, \underbrace{1, 1, \ldots, 1}_{23}].$$

There are 24 distinct orders, according as G is listed 1st, 2nd, ..., 24th. G will be pivotal when it is 7th through 19th, i.e, in 13 of the 24 orders. Hence the Gainesville bloc would have 13/24 = 54% of the voting power.

There is a simple formula for the voting power of a single voting bloc of size x in a voting body of size n with a winning quota q. First, define b = n - q + 1 to be the _blocking quota_, which is the number of votes necessary to keep a motion from passing. Then the

$$\text{power of a bloc of size x} = \begin{cases} \dfrac{x}{n-x+1} & \text{if } x \le b \\[2mm] \dfrac{b}{n-x+1} & \text{if } b \le x \le q \\[2mm] 1 & \text{if } q \le x. \end{cases}$$

For the above Florida example, n = 36, q = 19, b = 18, x = 13 < b. Hence the power of the bloc is

$$\frac{13}{36-13+1} = \frac{13}{24} = 54\%,$$

as we found directly, above.

Even more interesting things can happen when two voting blocs form within a voting body. For instance, suppose that in an environmental commission of size 11, voting by majority rule, there is an environmentalist bloc E of size e and an industrialist bloc I of size i. The members of each bloc vote together, but the two blocs are not assumed to be necessarily opposed. Table 1.2 illustrates the results of a power analysis for three different combinations of e and i.

TABLE 1.2

POWER OF TWO VOTING BLOCS IN AN 11-MEMBER VOTING BODY

Number of Bloc Members	% of Vote Controlled by E	% of Power Held by E	% of Vote Controlled by I	% of Power Held by I
e=2, i=2	18.2	19.4	18.2	19.4
e=4, i=2	36.4	47.6	18.2	14.3
e=4, i=4	36.4	30.0	36.4	30.0

Two small blocs can both gain power at the expense of other voters. One large bloc can gain power at the expense of a smaller bloc and other voters. Finally, two large blocs actually <u>lose</u> power to the other voters. One can see why this happens, for example, in

$$[6; \ 4, \ 4, \ 1, \ 1, \ 1].$$
$$\quad \text{E} \quad \text{I}$$

In situations where E and I are opposed, the individual voters who belong to neither bloc hold the balance of power.

The formula for the power of a bloc of size x when there are <u>two</u> blocs of sizes x and y in a voting body of size n and winning quota q, is only a little complicated. It uses the notion of "triangular numbers:"

$$T_a = \begin{cases} \dfrac{a(a+1)}{2} & \text{if } a \geq 0 \\ 0 & \text{if } a < 0. \end{cases}$$

In terms of triangular numbers, the power of a bloc of size x =

$$= \begin{cases} \dfrac{T_{q-y} + T_{b-y} - T_{q-x-y} - T_{b-x-y}}{2\,T_{q+b-x-y}} & \text{if } x \leq b \\[18pt] \dfrac{1}{2} + \dfrac{T_{b-y} - T_{q-x-y}}{2T_{q+b-x-y}} & \text{if } b \leq x \leq q \\[18pt] 1 & \text{if } q \leq x \end{cases}$$

Thus, the power of the bloc of size x depends not only on x, but also on the size y of the other bloc. In the example above, when x = 4 and y = 2, with q = 6 = b, the power of the bloc of size 4 is

$$\frac{T_{6-2} + T_{6-2} - T_{6-4-2} - T_{6-4-2}}{2\,T_{6+6-4-2}} = \frac{T_4 - T_0}{T_6}$$

$$= \frac{10 - 0}{21} = 0.476$$

as in Table 1.2.

In the course of designing a voting body, it may be wise to consider the effect which potential voting blocs could have on the distribution of power. Such potential voting blocs could arise in a variety of ways: from geographical proximity, political connections, common interests as polluters, and other common economic or environmental interests. For instance, Edwin Haefele in [4] does potential voting bloc analyses of a proposed Potomac Basin Commission, the San Francisco Bay Commission, a proposed Pennsylvania-New Jersey-Delaware air pollution agency, and the Minneapolis-St. Paul Metropolitan Council. He considers potential voting blocs arising both from political jurisdictions and from common interests.

1.4 Committees

In a voting body with a large or technical agenda, preliminary decisions are often referred to committees. Even in less complicated bodies, a steering committee may set the agenda before the main body meets. In such situations, a proposal may have to win the approval of a majority of the committee before it can even appear before the main body. It must then also be approved by a majority of the body. It is clear that members of the committee have more power over issues on which they have jurisdiction than other members of the voting body. How much more power do they have?

Consider a three-person committee in a nine-person voting body, where both the committee and the body act by majority rule. Call the committee members A's and the other members B's, so that the body has members AAABBBBBB.

To be approved, a proposal must have the support of at least five members, including at least two A's. There are

$$\binom{9}{3} = \frac{9!}{3!\,6!} = 84$$

possible orders* in which we can arrange the 3 A's and 6 B's. In how many of these will a B pivot? In order to be pivotal, a B must be preceded by exactly four letters, including either two A's or all three A's:

$$(AABB) \;\underline{B}\; (ABBB) \quad \binom{4}{2}\binom{4}{1} = 6\cdot 4 = 24 \text{ ways}$$

$$\text{or } (AAAB) \;\underline{B}\; (BBBB) \quad \binom{4}{3}\binom{4}{0} = 4\cdot 1 = \underline{4 \text{ ways}}$$
$$28 \text{ ways.}$$

As illustrated above, the theory of combinations tells us that these two possibilities can occur in exactly 28 ways. Hence B's will pivot in 28 orders, and A's in the other 84 − 28 = 56 orders. The power index of each A will be

$$\frac{1}{3}\cdot\frac{56}{84} = \frac{2}{9}$$

and the power index of each B will be

$$\frac{1}{6}\cdot\frac{28}{84} = \frac{1}{18}.$$

Thus, any committee member is <u>four times</u> as powerful as any non-committee member. When a committee structure is being chosen, or a body is turning over its agenda to a steering committee, this kind of power imbalance should be kept in mind.

There is a simple formula for the fraction of power held by the members (in toto) of a committee of <u>odd</u> size m in a voting body of <u>odd</u> size n, when both the committee and the body act by majority rule, as in the example above: the power of a committee of size m is

$$\frac{m + n}{2n}.$$

Thus the Shapley-Shubik index of each committee member is

$$\frac{1}{m}\cdot\frac{m+n}{2n},$$

---

*The symbol $\binom{n}{m}$ is the combinatorial coefficient which gives the number of ways in which m positions can be chosen from among n positions. It is calculated by the formula $\binom{n}{m} = \frac{n!}{m!\,(n-m)!}$.

and the Shapley-Shubik index of each non-committee member
is

$$\frac{1}{m-n} \left(1 - \frac{m+n}{2n}\right) = \frac{1}{2n} .$$

Finally, the _ratio_ of the power of a committee member to
that of a non-committee member is

$$\frac{1}{m} \cdot \frac{m+n}{2n} \Big/ \frac{1}{2n} = \frac{m+n}{m} = 1 + \frac{n}{m} .$$

Thus, for the above example, the indices are 2/9 and 1/18
and the ratio is 4. Taking another example, for a committee of size m = 5 in a voting body of size n = 35, the
power of a committee member is

$$\frac{1}{5} \cdot \frac{5+35}{70} = \frac{8}{70} ,$$

the power of a non-committee member is 1/70 , and a committee member has

$$1 + \frac{35}{5} = 8$$

times as much power as a non-committee member.

1.5 Decisions Made by Two or More Voting Bodies

In the United States Congress, a bill must be approved
by a majority of both the Senate and House of Representatives. (It must also, of course, be approved by the
President, or his veto must be over-ridden). A regional
water quality plan may have to be approved by each of
several committees, commissions and agencies. When two or
more bodies must each approve a proposal for it to pass,
how is power distributed among the members of the different
bodies?

Consider a system in which a proposal must be approved
by a majority of a three-person body (call its members A's)
and by a majority of a five-person body (call its members
B's). What is the Shapley-Shubik index of an A in this
scheme? Looking at all the members together, the letters
AAABBBBB can be ordered in

$$\binom{8}{3} = \frac{8!}{3!5!} = 56$$

different ways. For an A to pivot, she must be the second
A, and must be preceded by 3 or 4 or 5 B's:

$$(ABBB) \; \underline{A} \; (ABB) \quad \binom{4}{1}\binom{3}{1} = 4 \cdot 3 = 12 \text{ ways}$$

$$\text{or} \; (ABBBB) \; \underline{A} \; (AB) \quad \binom{5}{1}\binom{2}{1} = 5 \cdot 2 = 10 \text{ ways}$$

or (ABBBBB) $\underline{A}$ A $\begin{pmatrix} 6 \\ 1 \end{pmatrix} \begin{pmatrix} 1 \\ 1 \end{pmatrix} = 6\cdot1 = \underline{6 \text{ ways}}$

$$ 28 \text{ ways.}$$

Thus, an A will pivot in 28 of the 56 orders and a B will pivot in the other 28. Power is shared equally by the two bodies. Of course, because the first body is smaller, its individual members will have more power. The power index of an A is

$$\frac{1}{3} \cdot \frac{1}{2} = \frac{1}{6} \text{ ,}$$

while the power of a B is

$$\frac{1}{5} \cdot \frac{1}{2} = \frac{1}{10} \text{ .}$$

It is not hard to show that this result continues to hold when a proposal must be approved by each of two __odd__ sized bodies acting by majority rule: the bodies will share power equally. What is interesting is the effect that changing the voting rule for one body can have. Suppose, for instance, that our first body of A's decides to require the vote of __all three__ of its members for approval. The number of orders of A's and B's is still 56, but an A will now pivot when she is the __last__ A and is preceded by 3 or 4 or 5 B's:

(AABBB) $\underline{A}$ BB $\begin{pmatrix} 5 \\ 2 \end{pmatrix} \begin{pmatrix} 2 \\ 0 \end{pmatrix} = 10\cdot1 = 10 \text{ ways}$

or (AABBBB) $\underline{A}$ B $\begin{pmatrix} 6 \\ 2 \end{pmatrix} \begin{pmatrix} 1 \\ 0 \end{pmatrix} = 15\cdot1 = 15 \text{ ways}$

or (AABBBBB) $\underline{A}$ $\begin{pmatrix} 7 \\ 2 \end{pmatrix} \begin{pmatrix} 0 \\ 0 \end{pmatrix} = 21\cdot1 = \underline{21 \text{ ways}}$

$$ 46 \text{ ways.}$$

The A's together will now have 46/56 or 82% of the power. The power index of an A will increase to

$$\frac{1}{3} \cdot \frac{46}{56} = 0.274,$$

while that of a B will fall to

$$\frac{1}{5} \cdot \frac{10}{56} = 0.036.$$

The ratio of power between an A and a B will increase from

$$\frac{5}{3} = 1.67 \text{ to } \frac{23}{3} = 7.67.$$

In general, if one of two voting bodies requires a larger majority to pass a proposal, that body will have more power. This effect should be considered when a decision must be approved by several bodies in sequence. If a proposal requires unanimous approval by a planning body of three, for instance, and majority approval by an advisory committee of five, the planners will have 82% of the power.

When three or more bodies operating by majority rule must approve a proposal, the strictly symmetrical distribution of power no longer holds: The smaller bodies will have slightly more power. For example, Shapley and Shubik in their original article [12] considered the U.S. legislative scheme, omitting the possibility of overriding a Presidential veto, as a rule requiring majority approval of a bill by each of three bodies, of sizes 1 (the President), 101 (the Senate) and 435 (the House). In this scheme the President holds one-half the power, the Senate slightly over one-quarter, and the House slightly under one-quarter.

PROBLEMS

1) Verify the power indices given in Table 1.1 for
   a) [5 ; 3, 2, 1, 1]
   b) [5 ; 3, 2, 2, 1]

2) Verify the power indices for the 1958 European Council of Ministers given on page 4.

3) To which weighted voting bodies in Table 1.1 are the following voting bodies structurally equivalent? What are their power indices?
   a) [17 ; 11, 9, 8, 5]
   b) [17 ; 11, 9, 7, 6]
   c) [18 ; 11, 9, 7, 6]
   d) [19 ; 11, 9, 7, 6]

4) In a weighted voting body with four members, is it possible for all four members to have different power indices?

5) Verify directly that [4; 3, 1, 1, 1, 1] has power indices (.6, .1, .1, .1, .1) (page 7).

6) What is the percentage of voting power held by a single bloc of size 10 in a voting body of size 25 if the number of votes necessary to win is
   a) 13   b) 15   c) 17   d) 19?

7) Verify the formula for the power of a single voting bloc of size x in a body of size n with winning quota q (page 7). (Hint: The body is
   $$[q; x, \underbrace{1, \ldots, 1}_{n-x}].$$
   In which of the positions $1, 2, \ldots, n - x + 1$ will x be pivotal?)

8) Verify the figures in Table 1.2
   a) directly from the definition of the Shapley-Shubik power index
   b) using the formula on page 9.

9) Consider a voting body of size 40 with winning quota 21, containing two voting blocks, one of size 14 and the other of size 11. What percentage of the power will each of these two blocks have? Are these percentages higher or lower than the corresponding percentage of the votes? (For an application of this, see [14].)

10) To see why triangular numbers come into the formulas for two voting blocs on page 9, consider
$$[10;\ 4,\ 2,\ \underbrace{1,\dots,\ 1}_{11}].$$
$$\quad\ \ x\quad y$$
There are $13 \cdot 12 = 2T_{12}$ possible orderings, since both x and y may take positions 1 through 13. Represent these orderings as lattice points in the plane:

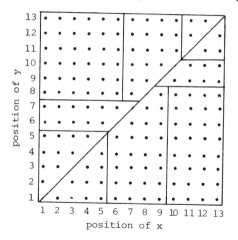

position of y

position of x

I have divided the points into regions. Label each region by X, Y, or 0 according as x, y, or an other voter is pivotal for the corresponding ordering. Check that the number of points in the regions labeled X is indeed $(T_8 - T_4) + (T_6 - T_2)$. This kind of diagram for the general case proves the formulas on page 9.

11) Calculate the power of an A and of a B in the body AAABB where a bill must be approved by at least three voters including at least two A's. Check that your figures agree with the formulas on pages 10 and 11.

12) Suppose that in order to be approved by the U.S. House of Representatives a bill must not only get a majority of the 435 Representatives, but also a majority of a

14

31-member Rules Committee (to get on the floor). What is the ratio of power of a Rules Committee member to a non-Committee member? How would this ratio change if the Rules Committee were enlarged to 45 members?

13) Verify that the total power of a committee of odd size m in a voting body of odd size n (both operating by majority rule) is indeed (m+n)/2n (page 10). (Hint: follow the reasoning on page 10 to show that total number of orderings in which a "B" is pivotal is

$$
\binom{\frac{n-1}{2}}{\frac{m+1}{2}}\binom{\frac{n-1}{2}}{\frac{m-1}{2}} + \binom{\frac{n-1}{2}}{\frac{m+3}{2}}\binom{\frac{n-1}{2}}{\frac{m-3}{2}} + \cdots + \binom{\frac{n-1}{2}}{\frac{2m}{2}}\binom{\frac{n-1}{2}}{0} = \frac{1}{2}\binom{n-1}{m}
$$

where the equality is by a combinatorial identity.)

14) Prove the combinatorial identity in 13) by considering the coefficient of x^m in the identity

$$
(1 + x)^{\frac{n-1}{2}} (1 + x)^{\frac{n-1}{2}} = (1 + x)^{n-1}.
$$

15) Verify that when a bill must be approved by each of two odd size bodies acting by majority rule, the bodies share power equally (page 12). (Hint: for each combined ordering, consider the corresponding reversed ordering.)

16) If a bill must be approved by at least 2 of 3 A's and at least 4 of 5 B's, what percentage of the power is held by the A's? What is the ratio of the power of an A to the power of a B?

17) Suppose that a bill must be approved by a president (P), a majority of a three-member Senate (SSS) and a majority of a five-member House (HHHHH). Calculate the power of P, of an S, and of an H. (This calculation is done in [12].)

BIBLIOGRAPHIC NOTES

In this chapter we have emphasized the Shapley-Shubik power index as the most widely accepted measure of voting power. Surveys of this index and some of its uses in political contexts appear in [10] and [11]. An example of the power of voting blocs appears in [14]. Sample uses in environmental contexts can be found in [4].

The only major competitor of the Shapley-Shubik index is a voting power index due to John Banzhaf in [1]. (This is the index used in New York court cases.) The Shapley-Shubik and Banzhaf indices are discussed and compared in

[2], [8], [13] and [15]. Included in [8] is a survey of methods for computing the indices for larger voting bodies, and many examples of weighted voting bodies. An elementary discussion of evaluating the Shapley-Shubik index as an integral appears in [16].

In interpreting some of this literature, the following definitions and terminology may be helpful. An n-person cooperative game is a set N of n players, together with a specification of the payoff v(S) which each coalition S N can obtain for its members. A simple game is an n-person cooperative game in which the value of each coalition is either 1 (the coalition is winning) or 0 (the coalition is losing). A proper simple game is one in which there are not two disjoint winning coalitions. The "voting games" we have been considering are proper simple games.

REFERENCES

1. John Banzhaf, "Weighted voting doesn't work: a mathematical analysis" Rutgers Law Review 19 (1965) 317-343.

2. S. J. Brams, Game Theory and Politics, Free Press, New York, 1975, Chapter 5.

3. S. J. Brams, Paradoxes in Politics: An Introduction to the Non-obvious in Political Science, Free Press, New York, 1976, Chapter 7.

4. E. Haefele, Representative Government and Environmental Management, Johns Hopkins University Press, Baltimore, 1973, Chapter 2.

5. R. W. Imrie, "The impact of the weighted vote on representation in municipal governing bodies of New York State" Annals of the New York Academy of Sciences 219 (1973) 192-99.

6. R. E. Johnson, "An analysis of weighted voting as used in reapportionment of county governments in New York State" Albany Law Review 34 (1969) 317-43.

7. A. K. Klevorick and G. H. Kramer, "Social choice in pollution mangement: the Genossenschaften" Journal of Public Economics 2 (1973) 101-146.

8. W. F. Lucas, Measuring Power in Weighted Voting Systems, Technical report #227, Department of Operations Research, Cornell University, Ithaca, New York 14853, 1976.

9. R. D. Luce and H. Raiffa. <u>Games and Decisions:</u>
    <u>Introduction and Critical Survey</u>, John Wiley, New
    York, 1957. Sections 11.4, 11.5 and Chapter 12.

10. W. H. Riker and P. Ordeshook, <u>An Introduction to</u>
    <u>Positive Political Theory</u>, Prentice-Hall, Englewood
    Cliffs, 1973. Chapter 6.

11. W. H. Riker and L. S. Shapley, "Weighted voting: a
    mathematical analysis for instrumental judgment" in
    Pennock and Chapman, eds., <u>Representation: Nomos X</u>,
    Atherton Press, New York, 1968.

12. L. S. Shapley and M. Shubik, "A method for evaluating
    the distribution of power in a committee system"
    <u>American Political Science Review</u> 48 (1954) 787-92.

13. P. D. Straffin, <u>Power Indices in Politics</u>,
    Mathematical Association of America Modules in Applied
    Mathematics, 334 Upson Hall, Cornell University,
    Ithaca, New York 14853, 1976.

14. P. D. Straffin, "The power of voting blocs: an
    example" <u>Mathematics Magazine</u> 50 (1977) 22-24.

15. P. D. Straffin, "Homogeneity, independence and power
    indices" <u>Public Choice</u> 30 (1977) 107-118.

16. P. D. Straffin, "Using integrals to evaluate voting
    power" <u>Two-Year College Mathematics Journal</u> 10 (1979)
    179-81.

2 Voting Methods for More than Two Alternatives

2.1 The Weaknesses of Sequential Pairwise Voting

In discussing voting power in Chapter One, we were looking only at the case where decisions were being made between two alternatives: a motion on the floor was to be voted on by a 'yes' or a 'no.' In most decision situations, the ultimate decision to be made is among more than two alternatives. Probably the most common way of making such a decision among multiple alternatives is to use a 'parliamentary procedure' to reduce the decision to a sequence of pairwise decisions. Then for pairwise decisions the power index considerations of Chapter One can tell us how influence is apportioned.

Unfortunately, reducing a decision among multiple alternatives to a sequence of pairwise decisions can have bizarre effects. Consider a case in which three voters must choose among four alternatives a, b, c and d, and suppose the voters have preferences among the alternatives as follows:

	1 Voter	1 Voter	1 Voter
Example 1	a	c	b
(3 Voters)	b	a	d
	d	b	c
	c	d	a

Thus, the first voter has alternative a as his first choice, b as his second choice, down to c as his last choice. Consider the result of sequential voting by majority rule, and suppose that the voters vote according to the above preferences. Suppose alternative a is first paired against b: the first and second voters will choose

19

a and the third will choose b, and a will win by a 2-to-1
vote. Then if alternative a is paired against c, c will
win, by a 2-to-1 vote. Finally, when alternative c is
paired against d, d will win, again by a 2-to-1 vote. The
sequence can be shown as

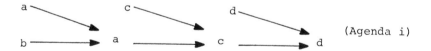

(Agenda i)

Hence, alternative d is chosen, in spite of the fact that
if we look back at the preference lists, we can see that d
seems to have little in its favor, and in fact the voters
are <u>unanimous</u> in preferring b to d. Sequential pairwise
voting can choose clearly undesirable alternatives.

Sequential voting is also highly sensitive to the
'agenda' - the order in which alternatives are introduced.
Consider the same voters with the same preferences, but
with three alternative agendas:

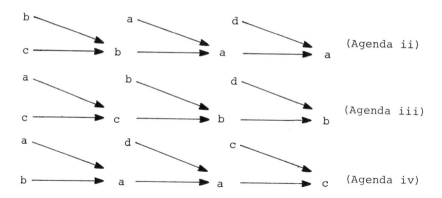

(Agenda ii)

(Agenda iii)

(Agenda iv)

Hence, in this example <u>any</u> <u>one</u> of the four alternatives can
be chosen, depending on the order in which the alternatives
are brought up for a vote. Chance, or sophisticated manipulation of the agenda, can have as much to do with the outcome as the preferences of the voters. With regard to ma-
nipulating the agenda, Duncan Black [2] has given one rule
of thumb: the later you bring up your favored alternative,
the better chance it has of winning. The idea is that if
there are other alternatives which might beat yours, those
others might themselves be beaten earlier in the voting.
When many voters reason this way, conflict over the agenda
can replace substantive conflict over the alternatives.

A third effect of sequential pairwise voting has been
carefully analyzed in a classic monograph by Robin

20

Farquharson [7]. Consider Agenda ii, which chose alternative a. Alternative a is the last choice of our third voter, and she might well ask if there is any way she could do better. There is, indeed. On the first vote in Agenda ii, our third voter helped alternative b to overcome alternative c. Suppose she had voted <u>insincerely</u> for c in the first vote instead of her true preference for b. The result would have been

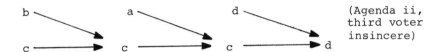

(Agenda ii, third voter insincere)

Our third voter has thus achieved her second choice instead of her last choice by this judicious bit of insincerity, and in the process has produced a rather undesirable social outcome. Sequential pairwise voting invites voters to think strategically and vote insincerely.

Given that sequential pairwise voting is unattractive in these kinds of ways, much attention has been given to analyzing and designing other voting rules for choosing among three or more alternatives. In this chapter we will look at a number of these rules and evaluate some of their strengths and weaknesses. The approach for evaluation will be to write down precisely a number of criteria which reasonable voting rules might be expected to satisfy, and investigate which voting rules satisfy which criteria. For instance, we have already seen one such criterion in our discussion of sequential pairwise voting. It is classically associated with the Italian economist Vilfredo Pareto (1848-1923):

<u>Pareto Criterion</u>: If <u>every</u> voter prefers an alternative x to an alternative y, a voting rule should not produce y as a winner.

Sequential pairwise voting violates this criterion.

This 'axiomatic' approach to the study of voting rules was pioneered by Kenneth Arrow [1], and the results of his and later analyses were both enlightening and discouraging: it is quite easy to write down a short list of reasonable-sounding criteria, and prove that no voting rule can satisfy all of them. Recent surveys of this kind of work can be found in [9], [16], [19], [22] and [23]. Hence, we cannot expect to find a perfect way of making decisions among three or more alternatives. Still, even in an imperfect world some methods may be better than others. We will try to find some of the better ones.

2.2 Plurality Voting

After sequential pairwise voting, plurality voting is perhaps the most widely used voting rule. Each voter votes for one alternative, and the alternative with the largest number of votes wins. Plurality voting eliminates the agenda effect of sequential pairwise voting, and satisfies the Pareto criterion. However, it has long been noted by political analysts that plurality voting has its own faults. The following example illustrates two of them. Consider a case in which 9 voters must choose from among three alternatives, a, b and c, and suppose that the voters have preferences among the alternatives as follows:

	3 Voters	2 Voters	4 Voters
Example 2	a	b	c
(9 Voters)	b	a	b
	c	c	a

One notable political example of this kind of situation was the 1970 New York Senatorial race between liberal Democrat Richard Ottinger (a), liberal Republican Charles Goodell (b), and Conservative James Buckley (c). Under plurality voting, alternative c wins with 4 first-choice votes, as Buckley won the Senatorial race. The possible inequity of this result comes from the fact that a 5-to-4 majority of voters rank c last, and would have preferred either of the other alternatives to c. In fact, if the voters had been asked to make pairwise decisions, one could picture the results as follows:

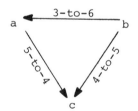

with b beating a by 6-to-3, b beating c by 5-to-4, and a beating c by 5-to-4. Alternative b, which came in last in the plurality vote, would thus have beaten either of the other alternatives in pairwise contests. According to a criterion advanced by the Marquis de Condorcet as early as 1785, b should have been the winner. This is the

Condorcet Winner Criterion: If there is an alternative x which could obtain a majority of votes in pairwise contests against every other alternative, a voting rule should choose x as the winner.

The alternative x of this criterion, if it exists, is unique and is called the <u>Condorcet winner</u>. Often there is no Condorcet winner. There is none in Example 1 at the beginning of this chapter, for instance, where the pattern of pairwise majority wins is

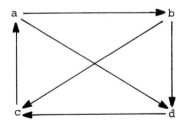

and every alternative loses a pairwise contest to some other alternative. The Condorcet criterion simply says that <u>if</u> there is a Condorcet winner, a voting rule should choose it.

Our first observation about Example 2 leads to a kind of reverse Condorcet criterion, termed the

<u>Condorcet Loser Criterion</u>: If an alternative y would lose in pairwise majority contests against every other alternative, a voting rule should <u>not</u> choose y as a winner.

Example 2 shows that plurality voting violates both of these Condorcet criteria. In addition, it is clear that when there are many alternatives, plurality voting can produce an extremely weak mandate. Consider, for instance:

	5 Voters	2 Voters	3 Voters	3 Voters	4 Voters
Example 3	a	b	c	d	e
(17 Voters)	b	c	b	b	b
	c	d	d	c	c
	d	e	e	e	d
	e	a	a	a	a

Here alternative a is the plurality winner, although 12 of the 17 voters rank it last. Alternative b comes in last under plurality voting, in spite of the fact that it is everyone's first or second choice, and is the Condorcet winner. In using only first place preferences, plurality voting does not take into account an equitable amount of information about the preferences of voters.

A common attempt to overcome these deficiencies is to combine plurality voting with a run-off between the top two vote-getters, if no alternative receives a majority of votes on the first ballot. This may not be much of an improvement: it would produce alternative e as the winner in

Example 3. Since alternative b is the Condorcet winner in Example 3, we see that plurality voting with a run-off still does not satisfy the Condorcet winner criterion. It does, however, satisfy the Condorcet loser criterion: the ultimate winner must win at least the pairwise contest of the run-off, and hence cannot lose all pairwise contests.

Unfortunately, this modest gain is effected at the cost of introducing a serious, perverse phenomenon. Consider the following:

	6 Voters	5 Voters	4 Voters	2 Voters
Example 4	a	c	b	b
(17 Voters)	b	a	c	a
	c	b	a	c

In the plurality contest, alternatives a and b are the top vote-getters, and a beats b in the run-off by a vote of 11-to-6 and, hence, a wins. Now suppose that the last two voters change their minds _in favor of alternative a_, so that they now have preference orderings of abc. A plurality election would now have alternatives a and c as the top vote-getters, and c would beat a in the run-off by a vote of 9-to-8. Hence, two voters deciding that they like alternative a better produces a win for c. In a recent article about this phenomenon, Doron and Kronick imagine a news announcement: "Candidate c won today, but if candidate a had received fewer first place votes, he would have won" [6]. The following criterion says that we should not allow this kind of perverse reaction in a voting rule --

Monotonicity criterion: If x is a winner under a voting rule, and one or more voters change their preferences in a way favorable to x (without changing the order in which they prefer any other alternatives), then x should still be a winner.

Straight plurality voting satisfies the Monotonicity condition, but plurality with a run-off violates it.

Finally, it is well known that plurality voting, with or without a run-off, often places voters in a strategic dilemma by tempting them to vote insincerely. If your favored alternative seems to have little chance of winning, or of placing in the top two, perhaps you should vote for a less favored alternative which does have a chance of winning. Thus in Example 2, Goodell voters were urged to support Ottinger in order to keep Buckley from winning. In Example 3, supporters of alternatives c and d would have been tempted to vote for b, thus possibly obtaining their second choice instead of their last choice.

2.3 Plurality Elimination Procedures

A number of voting procedures have been proposed which involve sequentially eliminating 'undesirable' alternatives until one alternative is able to obtain a majority of first place votes. The most widely used such procedure was popularized by Thomas Hare (see [6]). Hare's procedure was designed for the case in which a specified number m of alternatives is to be chosen from a collection of n alternatives. The general procedure is complicated, but when m = 1 it reduces to the following. Each voter writes down his or her preference ordering of the n alternatives, and an alternative is declared the winner if a majority of voters rank it first. If no alternative is ranked first by a majority of the voters, the alternative(s) with the smallest number of first place votes is (are) crossed out from all preference orderings, and first place votes are counted again. This is continued until a winner is selected. For instance, in Example 3, alternative b is eliminated first, yielding reduced preference orderings:

5 Voters	2 Voters	3 Voters	3 Voters	4 Voters
a	c	c	d	e
c	d	d	c	c
d	e	e	e	d
e	a	a	a	a

Since no alternative yet has a majority of first place votes, we continue and eliminate d, yielding

5 Voters	2 Voters	3 Voters	3 Voters	4 Voters
a	c	c	c	e
c	e	e	e	c
e	a	a	a	a

There is still no majority winner, and alternative e is crossed off. Alternative c is then declared the winner.

If we recall that alternative b was the Condorcet winner in this example, we see that the Hare system does not satisfy the Condorcet winner criterion; in fact, the Condorcet winner was the first alternative to be eliminated. Example 4 shows that the Hare system also does not satisfy the Monotonicity criterion.

An interesting elimination procedure, perhaps specifically applicable to the kinds of questions which arise in environmental planning, was first proposed by the psychologist Clyde Coombs [4]. Coombs argued that when we are seeking a kind of compromise solution which will not elicit violent opposition, we should eliminate first not the alternative with the smallest number of first place votes, but the alternative with the largest number of last place votes. Again, the procedure is to stop when one alterna-

25

tive commands majority support. Under the Coombs procedure, in Example 3 alternative a would be the first to be eliminated, leaving:

5 Voters	2 Voters	3 Voters	3 Voters	4 Voters
b	b	c	d	e
c	c	b	b	b
d	d	d	c	c
e	e	e	e	d

No alternative yet has a majority of first place votes, so e is eliminated, leaving:

5 Voters	2 Voters	3 Voters	3 Voters	4 Voters
b	b	c	d	b
c	c	b	b	c
d	d	d	c	d

Alternative b, with 11 first place votes, is now declared the winner.

Hence, in this example, the Coombs procedure does choose the Condorcet winner. We will see in the next section some data which indicate that the Coombs procedure is in general more likely to choose a Condorcet winner, when there is one, than the plurality or Hare procedures. However, it does not always do so:

	5 Voters	4 Voters	2 Voters	4 Voters	2 Voters	4 Voters
Example 5	a	a	b	b	c	c
(21 Voters)	b	c	a	c	a	b
	c	b	c	a	b	a

No alternative has a majority of first place votes, so alternative a with the largest number of last place votes is eliminated, and b wins. But in this example, alternative a is the Condorcet winner (it beats both b and c by a vote of 11-10).

Unfortunately, the Coombs procedure also fails to satisfy the Monotonicity condition. In the following example, the Coombs procedure eliminates alternative c and chooses a:

	5 Voters	2 Voters	4 Voters	2 Voters
Example 6	a	b	c	c
(13 Voters)	b	c	a	b
	c	a	b	a

If, however, the last two voters change their minds to favor alternative a over b, b will be eliminated and c will win.

In general, elimination procedures tend to consider information in too piecemeal a fashion. A good alternative may be eliminated early on the basis of partial information without considering the overall picture. We need to have a voting rule which considers information more uniformly.

2.4 The Borda Count

In 1781 Jean-Charles de Borda proposed his 'method of marks,' which has come to be known as the Borda count. In this voting system, each voter submits his or her preference ranking of the n alternatives to be considered. An alternative receives no points for being ranked last, one point for being ranked next to last, up to n-1 points for being ranked first. The points for each alternative are then summed across all voters, and the alternative with the highest total is the winner.

For instance, recall Example 1 at the beginning of this Chapter:

1 Voter	1 Voter	1 Voter
a	c	b
b	a	d
d	b	c
c	d	a

In the Borda count, alternative a receives 3 points from the first voter, 2 from the second, and 0 from the third, for a total of 5. Borda counts for all the alternatives are a:5, b:6, c:4 and d:3. Alternative b is the Borda winner.

The Borda count has a number of arguments in its favor. First of all, it uses information from the entire preference rankings of all voters - not just which alternative is ranked first or last - and it applies this information all at once instead of sequentially. Secondly, the Borda count chooses the alternative which occupies the highest position on the average in the voters' preference rankings, since the Borda count of an alternative x, divided by the number of voters, is just the average number of alternatives ranked below x. Thus in Example 1, alternative b has an average rank of two from the bottom, higher than any other alternative. This property could be important when we need a 'broadly acceptable' decision: having the highest average position in preference rankings might be a reasonable operational definition of 'broadly acceptable.'

For another justification of the Borda count, consider the results of the pairwise contests in Example 1, which can be shown as follows:

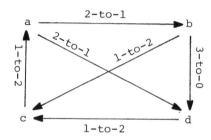

Notice that the total number of votes that alternative b
would get in pairwise contests is 1 + 2 + 3 = 6, exactly
its Borda count. This is always true when all voters have
strict preference orderings (no ties in the ordering).
Notice that, going back to the preference lists, we can
obtain alternative b's Borda count by simply counting the
number of letters below b in the three lists:

```
            d
    d       c
    c   d   a
```

But this just says that in pairwise contests alternative b
would get 1 vote against a, 2 against c, and 3 against d.
Hence, we can also interpret the Borda winner as the alternative which would do best on the average, in terms of numbers of votes, in pairwise contests with other alternatives.

The Borda count satisfies the Pareto condition, the
Condorcet loser condition, and the Monotonicity condition.
Condorcet was the first to point out that it does not sat-
isfy the Condorcet winner condition:

	3 Voters	2 Voters		
Example 7	a	b	Borda	a: 6
(5 voters)	b	c	counts	b: 7
	c	a		c: 2

In this example, alternative b is the Borda winner but a is
the Condorcet winner. Worse than that, alternative a has
an absolute majority of first place votes. The only reason
that b can win in the Borda count is that the presence of c
enables the last two voters to 'weight' their votes for b
over alternative a more heavily than the first three voters' votes for alternative a over b. The Borda count violates the following criterion, which is weaker than the
Condorcet criterion --

Majority criterion: If a majority of voters have an
        alternative x as their first choice, a voting
        rule should choose x.

In Example 7, our first three voters do have a natural defensive strategy. They can obtain alternative a as the Borda winner by insincerely listing their preferences as acb. In general, the Borda count is vulnerable to strategic manipulation in the following way: if a voter favors x and believes that y is the most dangerous competitor to x, he can minimize the risk that y will beat x by putting y at the bottom of his preference list. When the danger of this kind of strategic behavior was pointed out to Borda, his reply was, 'My scheme is only intended for honest men!' (See [2], page 238). A rewarding analysis of 'strategic tension' in voting with the Borda count has recently appeared as [12].

While none of the voting rules we have considered in Sections 2, 3 and 4 satisfy the Condorcet winner criterion, recent work indicates that the methods differ with respect to how often they fail to choose a Condorcet winner when there is one. The following figures, for instance, are due to Chamberlin and Cohen [3], who considered a fairly realistic spatial voting model with four alternatives and 21 voters, and asked what percentage of the time each of four voting methods will choose a Condorcet winner when there is one:

Plurality	53%
Hare	75%
Coombs	98%
Borda	83%

Coombs seems clearly superior in this respect, with Borda second and plurality a poor last. Moreover, as the number of voters increases, the performance of Coombs and Borda improves, while the performance of Hare and plurality declines.

2.5 Condorcet Voting Methods

Of the voting methods we have discussed so far, only sequential pairwise voting (with its many other flaws) satisfies the Condorcet winner criterion. In this section we will consider three additional voting methods which all satisfy this condition. Because they do, they are called Condorcet voting methods.

Probably the simplest suggestion was made by Duncan Black in [2]. If we value the Condorcet criterion, but believe that the Borda count also has advantages, we might do the following: in cases where there is a Condorcet winner, choose it; but in cases where there is no Condorcet winner, choose the Borda winner. We would require preference lists from the voters. We would then use the informa-

tion in the preference lists to construct a pairwise voting
diagram like the one we have seen earlier for Example 1:

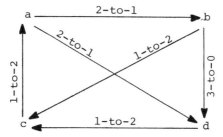

We would then check to see if one alternative beats all the
others in pairwise contests. If so, that alternative wins.
If not, we use the numbers in the diagram to compute the
Borda winner as in Section 2.4.

The Black rule is easy to implement, and satisfies the
Pareto, Condorcet loser, Condorcet winner and Monotonicity
criteria. It does not satisfy a plausible generalization
of the Condorcet criteria offered by John Smith [24] --

Smith's Generalized Condorcet criterion: If the alterna-
         tives can be partitioned into two sets A and B
         such that every alternative in A beats every
         alternative in B in pairwise contests, then a vo-
         ting rule should not select an alternative in B.

The Smith criterion implies both the Condorcet winner and
Condorcet loser criteria (take A to be the set which consists of only the Condorcet winner, or B to be the set
which consists of only the Condorcet loser). The following
example shows that Black's rule violates this criterion:

	1 Voter	1 Voter	1 Voter
Example 8	a	b	c
(3 Voters)	b	c	a
	x	x	x
	y	y	y
	z	z	z
	w	w	w
	c	a	b

If we partition the alternatives as A = [a, b, c] and B =
[x, y, z, w], then every alternative in A beats every
alternative in B by a 2-to-1 vote. Furthermore, there is
no Condorcet winner, since alternatives a and b and c beat
each other cyclically. When we compute Borda counts, we
get:

a	b	c	x	y	z	w
11	11	11	12	9	6	3

30

Hence, by Black's rule, alternative x is the winner. The special structure required in this and other similar examples does seem to indicate, however, that such situations are probably very rare.

A second ingenious Condorcet voting rule was proposed by E. J. Nanson in 1907. It is a Borda elimination scheme which sequentially eliminates the alternative with the lowest Borda count until only one alternative or a collection of tied alternatives remains. That this procedure will indeed always select the Condorcet winner, if there is one, follows from the fact that the Condorcet winner must garner more than half the votes in its pairwise contests with the other alternatives, and hence must always have a <u>higher than average</u> Borda count. Thus, it can never have the <u>lowest</u> Borda count, and can never be eliminated. Here is an example:

	3 Voters	4 Voters	4 Voters	4 Voters
Example 9	b	b	c	d
(15 Voters)	c	a	a	a
	d	c	b	c
	a	d	d	b

The pairwise voting diagram is:

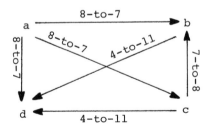

so that alternative a is the Condorcet winner. The Borda counts are a:24, b:25, c:26 and d:15. Hence, alternative c would be the Borda winner, and alternative a would come in next-to-last. However, under Nanson's procedure alternative d is eliminated and new Borda counts are computed:

3 Voters	4 Voters	4 Voters	4 Voters	
b	b	c	a	Borda a:16
c	a	a	c	counts b:14
a	c	b	b	c:15

Alternative b is now eliminated, and in the final round alternative a beats c by 8-to-7.

Since Nanson's procedure so cleverly reconciles the Borda count with the Condorcet criterion, it is a shame, but perhaps not surprising, to find that it shares the defect of other elimination schemes: it is not monotonic.

Here is an example offered by Fishburn [11]:

	8 Voters	5 Voters	5 Voters	2 Voters
Example 10	a	c	b	c
(20 Voters)	b	a	c	b
	c	b	a	a

The Borda counts are a:21, b:20, and c:19. Hence c is
eliminated, and then alternative a beats b by 13-to-7.
However, if the last two voters change their minds in favor
of alternative a over b, so that their preference ordering
is cab, the new Borda counts will be a:23, b:18 and c:19.
Hence b will be eliminated and then c beats a by 12-to-8.
The change in alternative a's favor has produced c as the
winner.

Our last Condorcet voting rule is a remarkably simple
rule, apparently first proposed by A. H. Copeland in 1950.
One looks at the results of pairwise contests between alternatives. For each alternative, compute the number of
pairwise wins it has minus the number of pairwise losses it
has. Choose the alternative(s) for which this difference
is largest. Thus, in Example 1:

Alternative	Wins	Losses	Copeland Score= Wins Minus Losses
a	2	1	1
b	2	1	1
c	1	2	-1
d	1	2	-1

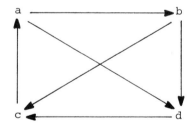

Alternatives a and b are the winners by the Copeland rule.
In Example 4,

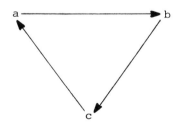

alternatives a, b and c are all chosen as winners. The Copeland rule is more likely than other methods to produce ties, since it does not take into account, for instance, the margins of victory in the pairwise contests, but only which alternative wins. (Thus, in Example 4, alternative a beat b by 11-to-6, b beat c by 12-to-5, and c beat a by only 9-to-8. The Borda count takes these margins into account and produces a as the winner.)

It is clear that if there is a Condorcet winner, Copeland's rule will choose it: the Condorcet winner will be the only alternative with all pairwise wins and no pairwise losses. The Copeland rule also satisfies all of the other criteria we have considered. If its indecisiveness can be tolerated, it seems to be a very good voting rule indeed.

Although in theory one could implement Copeland's rule just by holding pairwise votes between all pairs of alternatives, it is probably simpler to ask voters for preference orderings and then calculate the results of pairwise contests from the orderings. This also tends to increase consistency and discourage strategic manipulation.

The most serious problem with the Copeland rule is not a failure to meet any general criteria, but the fact that it may come into spectacular conflict with another reasonable voting rule - the Borda count. In particular, consider the following example:

	1 Voter	4 Voters	1 Voter	3 Voters
Example 11	a	c	e	e
(9 Voters)	b	d	a	a
	c	b	d	b
	d	e	b	d
	e	a	c	c

Copeland scores:	a: 2	Borda scores:	a: 16
	b: 0		b: 18
	c: 0		c: 18
	d: 0		d: 18
	e:-2		e: 20

Here alternative a is the Copeland winner and e comes in last, but e is the Borda winner and a comes in last. The two methods produce diametrically opposite results. If we try to ask directly whether a or e is better, we notice that the Borda winner e is preferred to the Copeland winner, alternative a, by eight of the nine voters! In a recent survey article in Scientific American [18], Riker and Niemi were disturbed enough by this phenomenon to almost suggest the following modification of the Copeland rule: Choose the Copeland winner unless it loses in a pairwise

contest with the Borda winner, in which case choose the
Borda winner. (This modification does not suggest how to
handle situations with a Copeland tie). Situations like
Example 11 lend credence to the suggestion.

2.6 Results of the Axiomatic Approach

The results of our axiomatic approach for evaluating
voting rules are summarized in Table 2.1. The logical re-
lations among the four Condorcet criteria are that a YES on
Condorcet winner implies a YES on Majority, and a YES on
Smith implies YES's on all the other three. I have underlined the NO's which I believe represent serious disadvan-
tages to certain voting rules.

It is clear from the discussion of the previous sections that all of these voting rules have some problems,
but the table supports our view that some methods are better than others. Sequential pairwise voting is bad because
of the agenda effect and the possibility of choosing a
Pareto dominated alternative. Plurality voting is bad because of the weak mandate it may give -- in particular, it
may choose an alternative which would lose to any other
alternative in a pairwise contest. Plurality with run-off
and the elimination schemes due to Hare, Coombs and Nanson
all fail to be monotonic: changes in an alternative's
favor can change it from a winner to a loser. Of these four
schemes, Coombs and Nanson are better than the others.
They generally avoid disliked alternatives, the Nanson rule
always detects a Condorcet winner when there is one, and
the Coombs scheme almost always does.

The Borda count takes positional information into full
account and generally chooses a non-disliked alternative.
Its major difficulty is that it can directly conflict with
majority rule, choosing another alternative even when a majority of voters agree on what alternative is best. Thus,
the Borda count would only be appropriate in situations
where it is acceptable that an alternative preferred by a
majority not be chosen if it is strongly disliked by a mi-
nority. The voting rules due to Copeland and Black appear
to be quite strong. The Black rule directly combines the
virtues of the Condorcet and Borda approaches to voting.
The Copeland rule emphasizes the Condorcet approach, but
Riker and Niemi have suggested how it might be modified to
avoid the most violent of conflicts with the Borda approach.

We have also seen how several of these voting rules
may be subjected to strategic manipulation at the hands of
voters who are willing to be insincere. In fact it is true
that all of these voting rules can be strategically manipulated. For a reference on this result, see the bibliographic notes at the end of the chapter.

TABLE 2.1

AXIOMATICS EVALUATION OF VOTING RULES

CRITERIA	VOTING RULES								
	Sequential pairwise	Plurality	Plurality with runoff	Hare	Coombs	Borda Count	Black	Nanson	Copeland
Pareto	NO	YES	YES	YES	YES	YES	YES	YES	YES
Monotonicity	YES	YES	NO	NO	NO	YES	YES	NO	YES
Condorcet loser	YES	NO	YES	YES	YES	YES	YES	YES	YES
Majority	YES	YES	YES	YES	YES	NO	YES	YES	YES
Condorcet winner	YES	NO	NO	NO	NO	NO	YES	YES	YES
Smith	YES	NO	NO	NO	NO	NO	NO	YES	YES
Remarks	Agenda effect					Usually chooses Condorcet winner	Violations of Smith rare		More likely to produce ties

Condorcet criteria [brackets Condorcet winner and Smith]

35

2.7 Application to Environmental Decision Making in the Bow River Valley

A classical example of a decision problem in water pollution control is the study of the hypothetical Bow River Valley by Dorfman and Jacoby [5]. A pollution control project is to be designed which will enable the Bow River to meet a water quality standard of 5 ppm dissolved oxygen. The major polluters along the river are the cities of Bowville (pop. 250,000) and Plympton (pop. 200,000) and the Pierce-Hall cannery. The goal of each of these three polluters is to maximize the difference between their individual benefit and individual cost for the pollution control project. There is also a water pollution control agency interested in maximizing the difference between total benefits and total costs. To begin to reconcile these four different objectives, Dorfman and Jacoby do a multi-objective analysis to determine five different Pareto-optimal pollution control options to achieve the required water quality (i.e. none of the options could be changed in a way favorable to some of the four objectives without being disfavorable to others). The five control options are denoted #8, #9, #11, #13 and #14 in the Dorfman-Jacoby study ([5], page 126).

We hypothesize that a policy advisory committee (PAC) is to recommend which of these five options to implement. The PAC is to consist of representatives from Bowville (B), Plympton (P), the cannery (C), and the water pollution control agency (W). For instance, it might have two representatives each from B and P, and one representative each from C and W, in which case it could be thought of as a weighted voting body:

[4 ; 2, 2, 1, 1].
  B P C W

Following the ideas of Chapter One, we can calculate the Shapley-Shubik power indices of the voters in this body. Such indices will only be applicable when pairwise decisions are to be made, but several of our multi-alternative voting rules do use pairwise comparisons, and in any case the results could be useful as a first approximation to the distribution of power. From Table 1.1 in Chapter One, we see that the Shapley-Shubik indices for this body are:

(1/3, 1/3, 1/6, 1/6),
  B   P   C   W

i.e., they happen to be in direct proportion to the numbers of votes.

Since deadlocks are possible in this body, it is proposed that the mayor of Bowville, the largest city, be given the power to break ties. From Chapter One we know that, at least for pairwise voting with no abstentions, this would be equivalent to changing the voting body to

[4 ; 3, 2, 1, 1]
 B P C W

The minimal winning coalitions would then be BP, BC, BW, and PCW, and the power indices would be:

(1/2, 1/6, 1/6, 1/6]
  B   P   C   W

It is concluded that the ability to break deadlocks is not worth the inequity of the resulting distribution of power, and the mayor should <u>not</u> be given the prerogative of breaking ties.

From Dorfman and Jacoby we have the following preferences for the five acceptable control options (#8, #9, #11, #13 and #14):

B	P	C	W
2 votes	2 votes	1 vote	1 vote
8	14	13	11
9	13	11-14	9-13
11	8-9-11	9	8
13		8	14
14			

The entries at the same level represent voter indifference among certain alternatives. We will assume that indifferent voters abstain in pairwise contests. The following analysis will illustrate how the voting rules in this chapter can be adjusted to deal with indifference and voting deadlocks. We will also see that different voting rules lead to different decisions in this environmental example.

The pairwise voting diagram for this example is

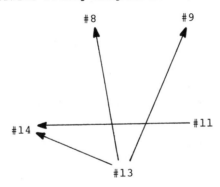

where all the arrows not shown represent tied votes. The
voting rules of this Chapter produce the following results:

1) Sequential pairwise voting. Control options #11 and
   #13 will enter the voting at some stage, and will then
   be deadlocked.

2) Plurality voting. Options #8 and #14 will be tied.
   The adoption of run-off or Hare elimination will produce the same deadlock.

3) Coombs elimination. Option #14 will be the first eliminated since it has the most last-place votes, yielding:

2 Votes	2 Votes	1 Vote	1 Vote
8	13	13	11
9	8-9-11	11	9-13
11		9	8
13		8	

   No option yet has a majority, and #8 (with 2-2/3 last-
   place votes) will be the next to go:

2 Votes	2 Votes	1 Vote	1 Vote
9	13	13	11
11	9-11	11	9-13
13		9	

   Control options #9 and #13 (2-1/2 last place votes
   each) are then eliminated, and alternative #11 wins.

4) Borda count. In the Borda count with ties, tied
   options are awarded the _average_ of the points which
   would normally be awarded to the places they hold.
   Thus in the preference list

   $$14$$
   $$13$$
   $$8-9-11$$

   options #8, #9, and #11 occupy positions worth 0 + 1 +
   2 = 3 points, so they are each awarded one point. The
   Borda counts are:

#8	#9	#11	#13	#14
11	11 1/2	12 1/2	14 1/2	10 1/2

   and option #13 is the Borda winner.

5) Black. Since there is no Condorcet winner (#13 ties
   #11, but does not beat it), the Black rule awards the
   decision to the Borda winner, #13.

6) Nanson elimination. Under Nanson's elimination scheme,
   option #14, which has the lowest Borda count, is eliminated, and revised Borda counts are #8:8, #9:8 1/2,
   #11:9 and #13:10 1/2. Option #8 is then eliminated,

yielding new Borda counts of #9:5 1/2, #11:6 and #13:6
1/2. Option #9 is then eliminated and then #11 and #13
tie.

7) The Copeland scores are

   #8: 0 - 1 = -1
   #9: 0 - 1 = -1
   #11: 1 - 0 = 1
   #13: 3 - 0 = 3
   #14: 0 - 2 = -2

with alternative #13 as the Copeland winner.
These results can be summarized as follows:

Voting Method	Winner(s)
Sequential pairwise	11, 13
Plurality	8, 14
Plurality with run-off	8, 14
Hare	8, 14
Coombs	11
Borda count	13
Black	13
Nanson	11, 13
Copeland	13

What is clear, of course, is that the voting method used
has a major effect upon the decision reached.

2.8 Application to Multi-Objective Decisions by a Single Decision-Maker

We have been concerned in this Chapter with a collection of voters who must decide among several alternatives.
The methods we have discussed are also applicable to a
single decision-maker who must decide among several alternatives, but who is trying to satisfy multiple objectives.
Consider, for instance, the following kind of problem from
[15]. A decision-maker must choose among four alternatives
a, b, c and d. In making his decision, he must consider
the performance of the alternatives with respect to four
objectives. The objectives are of such a nature that
numerical measures of performance are difficult to come by
(e.g., improved environmental quality, minimal social dis-
ruption, high aesthetics, etc), but it does seem possible
to at least rank how the alternatives perform according to
the different objectives. The performance results are:

1st Objective	2nd Objective	3rd Objective	4th Objective
a	d	b	c
b	a	d	d
c	b	a	a
d	c	c	b

39

Thus, with respect to the first objective, alternative a performs best and alternative d performs worst, while with respect to the second objective d performs best and c worst.

If all of the objectives are of equal importance, we could simply consider each objective as a 'voter', and use a (preferably good) voting rule from this Chapter to make the decision. Usually, however, some ojectives will be more important than others. In such a case, we can still apply our methods if we feel justified in 'weighting' the different objectives. For instance, if we feel that the first objective is quite important, we might assign weights of 3, 2, 2, 1 and think of the objectives as voters in a weighted voting body [5 ; 3, 2, 2, 1]:

3 Voters	2 Voters	2 Voters	1 Voter
a	d	b	c
b	a	d	d
c	b	a	a
d	c	c	b

If we are using a voting rule which relies on pairwise comparisons (e.g, Copeland's rule), we should be careful to check the <u>power</u> of objectives. In this case the Shapley-Shubik indices of the objectives are:

(5/12, 3/12, 3/12, 1/12).

If this does not differ too drastically from our sense of relative importance, we can proceed. If we are using a voting rule which does not rely on pairwise comparisons (e.g., the Borda count), we can omit this check. In any case, it would be wise to do a 'sensitivity analysis', experimenting with several sets of weights to see if the result changes with nearby weight assignments.

In choosing a voting rule to use, note that the criteria we used to evaluate voting rules still make good sense in the present context. The Pareto criterion says we should not choose an alternative if another alternative performs better with respect to <u>every</u> objective. The Monotonicity criterion says that if we choose an alternative, and then the performance of that alternative with respect to some objective is <u>improved</u> (the performance of other alternatives remaining the same), we should still choose it. The Condorcet criterion says that if some alternative performs better than any other alternative, measured by a weighted sum across objectives, than it should be our choice. Violations of the Pareto and Monotonicity criteria seem to be particularly serious in this context.

In the above example the diagram of pairwise contests is

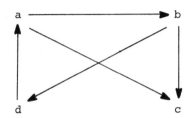

where the omitted arrow represents a tie between alternatives d and c. Plurality voting considers only the best
alternative with respect to each objective, and chooses
alternative a, which performs best with respect to the most
important objective. Hare elimination eliminates first c
and then b, and then chooses d over a. Coombs elimination
-- ruling out alternatives which perform very badly with
respect to enough criteria -- eliminates c and then chooses
a.

The Borda counts of the alternatives are a:16, b:14,
c:6 and d:12, so that alternative a is the Borda winner.
Since there is no Condorcet winner, a also wins by Black's
rule. Nanson elimination rules out alternative c and then
b, and ends by choosing d over a. Finally, Copeland's rule
produces a tie between alternatives a and b.

These results can be summarized as follows:

Decision Method	Winner(s)
Plurality	a
Plurality with run-off	d
Hare	d
Coombs	a
Borda count	a
Black	a
Nanson	d
Copeland	ab

Once again, the choice of decision rule is important for
the outcome. The decision rules which I have argued have
preferred properties -- Coombs, Borda count, Black and
Copeland -- seem to agree on alternative a as the optimal
outcome, whereas other decision rules often select d. Of
course, the proper procedure for this kind of decision
problem is to select a decision rule in advance, because of
its desirable properties, and then abide by the outcome it
produces.

PROBLEMS

1) Prove that plurality voting satisfies the Pareto cri-
    terion.

2) Prove that plurality voting satisfies the Monotonicity
    criterion.

3) If there are only three alternatives, is the Hare elimination procedure equivalent to plurality voting with a runoff?

4) Verify that the Borda count satisfies the Pareto, Condorcet loser, and Monotonicity criteria.

5) Verify that the Majority criterion is weaker than the Condorcet winner criterion, i.e. that any voting rule which satisfies the Condorcet criterion, must also satisfy the Majority criterion.

6) Verify that the Black rule satisfies the Pareto, Condorcet loser and winner, and Monotonicity criteria.

7) Verify that the Copeland rule satisfies all of the criteria considered.

8) Complete the verification of the entries in Table 2.1.

9) In the example of Section 2.7, calculate the outcomes with respect to all voting rules considered, if the PAC should operate as the weighted voting game [4; 3, 2, 1, 1]. Make a table like the one on page 39. Which voting rules translate B's increased power into selection of alternatives more favorable to B? Are there any voting rules which translate B's increased power into an outcome _less_ favorable to B?

10) In the example of Section 2.8, do a 'sensitivity analysis' by considering the weighted voting games [3; 1, 1, 1, 1], [4; 2, 2, 1, 1] and [5; 4, 2, 2, 1] and the resulting effect on the outcomes for the various voting rules. As the weight of the first objective is increased, do the various voting rules select alternatives which satisfy that objective better?

11) We have seen that some voting rules can be strategically manipulated, and I claimed that this is true of all the ones we have considered. Examine strategic manipulation of Copeland's rule in Example 11.
   a) Show that if one of the four voters with preference order c d b e a insincerely listed his preferences as c b d e a, Copeland's rule would give a tie between a and b, which our voter would prefer to a win for a.
   b) Show that if one of those voters insincerely listed e c d b a, then Copeland's rule would give a win for e, which our voter would prefer to a win for a.

12) Kenneth Arrow's most famous condition (see page 21) might be phrased in our context as follows:

Independence-of-Irrelevant-Alternatives Criterion:

If a voting rule chooses x as a winner, and some alternative y is then removed from the set of alternatives, the voting rule should still choose x as a winner.

Show that none of the voting rules we have considered satisfies this criterion. Arrow's non-existence result is a consequence of the stringency of this criterion. (Hint: you will need nine counter-examples. Examples given in this chapter will do for all nine. This should not prevent you from making up possibly simpler counter-examples of your own!)

13) Peter Fishburn [11] has extended the Condorcet winner idea into a voting rule as follows. Suppose we are in a voting situation where no pairwise ties between alternatives are possible (the Fishburn rule handles pairwise ties in a rather complicated way). Declare x to be a winner if for any other alternative y, either x beats y directly in a pairwise contest or x beats another alternative z which in turn beats y. Hence Fishburn's rule, like Copeland's, depends only on the diagram of pairwise wins.

a) It is clear that Fishburn's rule satisfies the Condorcet winner criterion. Show that it also satisfies the Pareto, Monotonicity, and Smith criteria (hence all the criteria we have considered).

b) What is the set of Fishburn winners for Example 1?

c) Show that in Example 11, all alternatives are Fishburn winners.

d) Show that what you found in b) and c) is true in general: every Copeland winner is always a Fishburn winner. In particular, this shows that the set of Fishburn winners is always non-empty, a fact which is not at all obvious from the definition! It also shows that the Fishburn rule is less decisive than the Copeland rule, which was already fairly indecisive. (Hint: if x is not a Fishburn winner, then there is another alternative y such that $y \longrightarrow x$ and it is never true that $x \longrightarrow z \longrightarrow y$. Show that y has a higher Copeland score than x.)

The result in d) is known as Landau's Theorem. For a history of this theorem and other results about this voting rule, see Stephen Maurer, "The King Chicken Theorems," Mathematics Magazine 53 (1980) 67-80.

BIBLIOGRAPHIC NOTES

Modern social choice theory is the interweaving of two strands. The first stems from the work of Kenneth Arrow [1], and its typical result is an 'impossibility theorem': it is impossible for a voting method for more than two alternatives to satisfy all of m reasonable criteria. Arrow's original work concerned the impossibility of a social decision function, which will use individual preference orderings over n alternatives to produce a complete social preference ordering over the n alternatives in a reasonable way. By contrast, we have been concerned with what is usually known as a social choice function, which uses individual preference orderings only to choose a socially 'best' alternative. References are [9], [16], [19], [22] and [23]. A related result due to Gibbard and Satterthwaite ([13] and [21]) is that all 'reasonable' social choice functions are strategically manipulable.

The other strand of social choice theory is the part we have emphasized here -- the study of the properties of specific voting systems. This strand stems from the work of Duncan Black [2]. Black also gives in [2] an excellent survey of the early history of this kind of thinking, emphasizing the contributions of Borda (1781), Condorcet (1785), and C. L. Dodgson (Lewis Carroll), and reproducing fully Dodgson's 1876 phamphlet, 'A method of taking votes on more than two issues'. Recent work of this kind can be found in [8], [10], [11], [17], [18], [20] and [24]. The 'Condorcet loser criterion' of our Section 2.2 was apparently first formally introduced by Peter Fishburn.

Dorfman and Jacoby's Bow River Valley example has been analyzed from a political point of view by several other authors. See, for example, Haefele in [14].

REFERENCES

1. K.J. Arrow, Social Choice and Individual Values, John Wiley, New York, 1963 (First published 1951).

2. Duncan Black, The Theory of Committees and Elections, Cambridge University Press, 1968 (First published 1958).

3. J. R. Chamberlin and M. D. Cohen, 'Toward applicable social choice theory: a comparison of social choice functions under spatial model assumptions,' Institute of Public Policy Studies, University of Michigan, 1978.

4. C. H. Coombs, A theory of Data, John Wiley, New York, 1964, Chapter 18.

5. R. Dorfman and H. D. Jacoby, 'An illustrative model of river basin pollution control,' in Dorfman, Jacoby and Thomas, eds., <u>Models for Managing Regional Water Quality</u>, Harvard University Press, 1972, pp. 84-141.

6. G. Doron and R. Kronick, 'Single transferable vote: an example of a perverse social choice function,' <u>American Journal of Political Science</u> 21 (1977) 303-311.

7. Robin Farquharson, <u>Theory of Voting</u>, Yale University Press, 1969.

8. P. C. Fishburn, 'A comparative analysis of group decision methods' <u>Behavioral Science</u> 16 (1971) 538-544.

9. P. C. Fishburn, <u>The Theory of Social Choice</u>, Princeton University Press, 1973.

10. P. C. Fishburn, 'Paradoxes of voting,' <u>American Political Science Review</u> 68 (1974) 537-46.

11. P. C. Fishburn, 'Condorcet social choice functions,' <u>SIAM Journal on Applied Mathematics</u> 33 (1977) 469-89.

12. Roy Gardner, 'The Borda game,' <u>Public Choice</u> 30 (1977) 43-50.

13. A. Gibbard, 'Manipulation of voting schemes: a general result,' <u>Econometrica</u> 41 (1973) 587-602.

14. E. Haefele, <u>Representative Government and Environmental Management</u>, The Johns Hopkins University Press, 1973, Chapter 3.

15. J. C. Holmes, 'An ordinal method of evaluation,' <u>Urban Studies</u> 9 (1972) 179-91.

16. Dennis Mueller, 'Public choice: a survey,' <u>Journal of Economic Literature</u> (1976) 395-433.

17. Dennis Mueller, <u>Public Choice</u>, Cambridge University Press, 1979.

18. R. G. Niemi and W. H. Riker, 'The choice of voting systems,' <u>Scientific American</u> 234 (1976) 21-27.

19. C. R. Plott, 'Axiomatic social choice theory: an overview and interpretation,' <u>American Journal of Political Science</u> 20 (1976) 511-96.

20. J. Richelson, 'A comparative analysis of social choice functions,' <u>Behavioral Science</u> 20 (1975) 331-37.

21. M. A. Satterthwaite, 'Strategy-proofness and Arrow's conditions: existence and correspondence theorems for voting procedures and social welfare functions,' Journal of Economic Theory 10 (1975) 187-217.

22. A. K. Sen, Collective Choice and Social Welfare, Holden-Day, San Francisco, 1970.

23. A. K. Sen, 'Social choice theory: a reexamination,' Econometrica 45 (1977) 53-89.

24. John H. Smith, 'Aggregation of preferences with variable electorate,' Econometrica 41 (1973) 1027-41.

3 Recent Approaches to Voting Using Intensities of Preferences

The voting rules considered in Chapter Two rely only on the order in which voters rank alternatives. They do not take into consideration that a voter may not just prefer a to b to c, but feel that there is more of a difference between b and c than between a and b. It may be desirable to take such relative intensity of preferences into consideration. Consider the following example:

```
  1 Voter        1 Voter        1 Voter
    a┌             b┌             c┌
    b├

                   c├             a├
    c└             a└             b└
```

The positions of the alternatives on the vertical lines represent intensity of preferences. Thus, the first voter prefers alternative a to alternative b only slightly, but much more strongly prefers both of them to c. If only preference orderings were taken into account, the symmetry of the situation would make it indeterminate -- a, b and c would tie by any non-discriminatory voting method. Given relative intensities, it seems clear that b is the best social choice.

The relative intensities illustrated in the example are known as <u>cardinal utilities</u>, as distinct from <u>ordinal utilities</u> which only tell the order in which alternatives are ranked. There is considerable debate about what cardinal utilities mean, and hence how they should be obtained. One school of thought, developed by von Neumann and Morgenstern in [17] as a foundation for the mathematical theory of games, uses lotteries. If for our first voter we place alternative b 4/5 of the way towards alternative a, it is because the voter would be indifferent between the choice of b for certain, or a lottery which would yield alternative a 4/5 of the time and c 1/5 of the time. Another approach holds that voters may be able to answer consistently direct questions about relative intensities, and we put b where we do because the first voter can say meaningfully: "My preference for b over c is four times as strong as my preference for a over b". (See the discussion in [7].) Yet another approach has the voter think of the vertical scale as a "feeling thermometer" on which to mark how "warm" or "cold" he feels toward each alternative (see [9], for instance). His feelings are then usually "normalized" by expanding his scale to put his most preferred alternative at the top and his least preferred alternative at the bottom of the scale. Finally, a voter may be asked to take 100 points and distribute them among the alternatives in a way which expresses his preferences [12]. Our first voter might have given 0 points to c, 44 points to b and 56 points to a.

Of these approaches, the von Neumann-Morgenstern interpretation is probably the most operationally meaningful, but actually measuring utility by this method requires that voters be able to think consistently about rather complicated kinds of lotteries. In any case, it is far from clear that any two of the above approaches would yield the same result. Because of these difficulties, we will consider in this chapter only two simpler methods for using intensities of preferences in voting. Both of these methods have been suggested quite recently, and their properties are the subject of current research. I believe they have great promise, but they should be considered as still in the "experimental" stage.

In the first method, a voter is not asked about his preference ordering at all, but simply which alternatives he "approves of." We will see that this scheme of approval voting gives voters at least a limited chance to say something about their relative intensities of preferences, and considerably reduces possibilities of stategic insincerity. In the second method, voters are asked to place dollar bids on the alternatives. Very recently, a clever enforcement scheme has been developed which encourages voters to place their bids sincerely. Because the scheme yields honest revelation of preferences, it is called a preference revealing or incentive compatible process. Problems with the implementation of this newer scheme are discussed in the concluding section.

3.2 Approval Voting

Under approval voting, each voter can give one vote each to as many of the n alternatives under consideration as he or she wishes. The alternative which receives the largest number of these "approval votes" wins. For instance, consider the Dorfman-Jacoby water pollution control example in Section 2.7:

B (2 Votes)	P (2 Votes)	C (1 Vote)	W (1 Vote)	Approval Votes
8	14	13	11	#8: 2
9	13	11-14	9-13	#9: 3
11	8-9-11	9	8	#11: 4
13		8	14	#13: 2
14				#14: 3

We will see using Dorfman and Jacoby's cost-benefit figures that a reasonable result of approval voting might be that each voter votes for the alternatives above the dividing line shown. Alternative #11 would thus be chosen.

Approval voting is very easy to use, and has the advantage of usually choosing an alternative which is acceptable to many voters. It has recently been the subject of considerable investigation by political scientists (see the bibliographic notes), who are particularly interested in its potential use in Presidential primaries.

Exactly how might approval voting use intensities of preferences? To see that, consider the question of how a voter should cast his approval votes. Suppose that the voter has cardinal utilities (defined in Section 3.1), however determined, for the alternatives, and his goal is to cast his approval votes in a way which will maximize his expected utility. At least, if our voter has no knowledge of what the outcome of voting is likely to be, Weber [18] and Merrill [11] have shown that the strategy which will maximize his expected utility is to vote for all alternatives with utility above his average utility level for the alternatives. For the Dorfman-Jacoby example, cardinal utilities (represented by cost-benefit figures) are as follows:

49

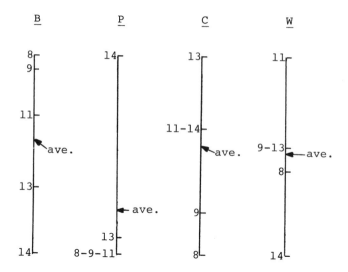

The average utility of the five alternatives is shown on
each of the preference scales. If voters follow Weber and
Merrill's strategy, they will vote as we postulated above.
Because the Weber-Merrill strategy derives from averaging
cardinal utilities, approval voting by this strategy specifically relies on preference intensities.

Approval voting is subject to strategic manipulation.
For instance, voter P could cast her two votes for #13 as
well as #14, and thereby secure a tie between #13 and #11,
which she would prefer to a victory for #11. (Admittedly,
the motivation to do this is quite weak in this example).
Brams and Fishburn [3] have shown that, in a precise sense,
approval voting is less subject to strategic manipulation
than, for instance, plurality voting. When strategic manipulation is possible, it usually appears in a fairly mild
form -- a voter will react to strategic considerations by
setting his cutoff point higher or lower on his preference
scale than he would otherwise. There is not the strong
temptation to pass over your first choice and vote for your
second, as there often is under plurality voting, or to
rank your second choice last, as in the Borda count.

3.3 Voting by Bids

Although a voter whose preference order among three
alternatives is abc may be able to say that he prefers alternative a to alternative b twice as much as he prefers b
to c, he will not be able to say convincingly that he prefers alternative a to alternative b more than another voter
prefers b to a. The problem of interpersonal comparison of
utilities appears to be intractable. A traditional ap-

proach to this problem has been to assume that there is
some commodity, usually money, which has the same value to
all voters, and then measure other utilities by this standard. Thus the voters can communicate intensities of preferences by <u>bidding money</u> for alternatives. The assumption that money has the same worth to all voters is almost
certainly false, especially, for instance, if voters have
widely different incomes. Hence, eventually we will have
to face the problem of weighting voters' monetary bids
according to some economic or ethical criterion, and we are
unlikely to find any completely satisfactory criterion.

However, suppose temporarily that money can be used as
a standard (i.e., assume that our voters are economically
and psychologically homogeneous). How should we then design
a scheme of voting by bids? The most obvious answer is to
have each voter bid for each alternative, and choose the
alternative with the highest total bid. It is convenient
to allow negative bids, and to ask each voter to arrange
his bids to add to zero. Thus a voter who prefers alternative c slightly to b, and strongly prefers both of them
to alternative a, might arrange his bids with a: -$40,
b: $15 and c: $25.

At this point the problem of honesty, which was only a
nagging difficulty for the ordinal voting methods of
Chapter 2 or for approval voting, becomes critical. Without some kind of enforcement procedure our voter might very
well arrange his bids with a: -$40,000, b: $15,000 and c:
$25,000. The simplest enforcement mechanism is simply to
<u>collect</u> the bids made for the winning alternative.
"Collecting" a negative bid, of course, means paying the
voter that amount. Since the winning alternative will have
a positive total bid, we will always collect more than we
will pay out.

Let us consider an example (bids in dollars):

	a	b	c
Voter 1	-40	15	25
Voter 2	20	0	-20
Voter 3	-10	25	-15
Voter 4	-20	-15	35
Voter 5	30	-35	5
	-20	-10	+30

In submitting these bids, Voter 1 is saying that he is indifferent among three possibilities: having alternative a
win and being paid $40, having b win and paying $15, and
having c win and paying $25. It is thus worth $65 to him
to have c chosen instead of a, but only $10 to have c cho-
sen instead of b. In this example alternative c would be
declared the winner. $25 would be collected from Voter 1,

$35 from Voter 4, and $5 from Voter 5. $20 of the money collected would go to compensate Voter 2, and $15 to compensate Voter 3. The voters who favor alternative c thus pay for it, and voters who dislike it are reimbursed. The $30 collected but not disbursed represents the cost of decision making.

Taking cardinal utilities into account, it does seem clear that alternative c should be selected. Notice, however, that under plurality voting, alternatives a and c would tie, and then a would beat c in a run-off. Borda count, Black's method and Copeland's method all produce a three-way tie among the alternatives.

Unfortunately, we have not yet checked that this enforcement scheme of collecting bids for the winning alternative will induce voters to make honest bids. It does not. It does eliminate the problem of extreme over-bidding, but in doing so it introduces a problem of under-bidding long familiar to economists. Suppose the above table represents sincere bids, and consider how voters might be tempted to bid insincerely. Voters 1 and 4 obtain their first choice of alternative c, but they must pay a pretty good amount to get it. If it is clear to them that c will win by a healthy margin, they can save money by bidding less for c. Voter 1, for instance, could save money by bidding only a: -15, b: 5 and c: 10. Alternative c would still win, and now he would pay only $10. Similarly, Vote 4 could save money while still obtaining alternative c by bidding a: -10, b: -5 and c: 15. Now consider what happens if _both_ Voters 1 and 4 adopt this approach:

	a	b	c	
Voter 1	-15	5	10	(insincere)
Voter 2	20	0	-20	
Voter 3	-10	25	-15	
Voter 4	-10	- 5	15	(insincere)
Voter 5	30	-35	5	
	+15	-10	- 5	

Voters 1 and 4 in their individual attempts to better themselves have lost alternative c (and the money they gained is less than it was worth to them to have c instead of a). Socially, a non-optimal choice has been made because of this insincerity.

Notice that the same effect could have been brought about by Voters 2, 3 and 5 reasoning that: "Since c is clearly going to win, why don't I put a large negative bid on c and collect a bundle?" In fact, if we collect the bids made for the winning alternative, _every_ voter will be tempted to underbid for the alternative he believes will win. If even some of them yield to temptation, we are likely to end up selecting an inferior alternative. In the economic theory of public goods, this problem has long been known as the <u>free rider problem</u>. If the selection of alternative c is a public good which can be obtained if it is paid for, every voter will be tempted to "free ride" and let the other voters pay for it.

Given that this most obvious enforcement scheme does not induce sincerity of bids, is there any scheme which does? It is interesting that until recently it was almost universally believed that no such scheme was possible. However, there is such a scheme, and we will discuss it in Section 3.5. First, however, we will consider in the next section some historical background which is interesting in its own right, and which will aid in understanding the reasoning in Section 3.5.

3.4 Vickrey's Scheme for Sealed Bidding

In a formidably titled paper in 1961, William Vickrey [16] considered the familiar system of awarding leases or contracts on the basis of sealed bids. Suppose, for example, that a government wishes to sell a lease for off-shore oil drilling. It solicits sealed bids from interested companies and awards the lease to the highest bidder, which must pay, of course, the amount it bid. Suppose there are three interested companies, and their <u>true values</u> for the lease are:

Company	True Value
1	$25,000
2	$24,000
3	$23,500

The true value of the lease to a company can best be understood as the price such that the company is indifferent between getting the lease at that price, and not getting it at all. True values are, of course, determined by many factors including expected cost of development, desired rate of profit, and alternatives available to the company.

Given these true values, how much will the companies bid? We can definitely be sure that each company will bid an amount strictly <u>less</u> than its true value: a bid of the true value would make it indifferent as to whether it got the lease or not. How much less is a complicated question. What each company bids will be determined in large part by how much it expects other companies will bid. One tries to bid just enough to beat the opposition, knowing that they are trying to do the same. Company 1, for instance, might believe that it could get away with $23,000, underestimating the other companies' desires and caution. Actual bids might look like:

53

Company	Bid
1	$23,000
2	$23,100
3	$23,200

In this case, Company 3 wins the lease. But notice that this outcome is inefficient: the lease goes to the company which values it least, and the government gets a comparatively low price. If the lease had gone to Company 1 at $24,000 both the government and the economy would have been better off.

The problems with this standard sealed bidding scheme appear very much like the problems we noted in voting by bids when bids for the winning alternative are collected. All agents underbid, all agents are involved in complicated strategic guesses as to how much they can underbid, and socially inefficient outcomes may result.

Vickrey's contribution was an excellent, simple suggestion as to how these problems can be remedied for the sealed bidding case. In this suggestion is the seed of the remedy for the analogous problems with voting by bid. Vickrey suggested that the lease still be awarded to the highest bidder, but that it pay only the amount bid by the second highest bidder! To see that this scheme does more than just have the government lose money, we must look at its motivational consequences.

What Vickrey noticed was that, under this scheme, each company will be motivated to bid exactly its true value, and that this will be true regardless of what it expects other companies to bid. Let us consider, for instance, Company 1 in our example. First, would Company 1 ever wish to bid more than $25,000? The answer is no. The only advantage in doing this would be if Company 1 could win the lease by bidding more, whereas it would not win it with the $25,000 bid. But this would only be true if another company bid over $25,000. Hence if Company 1 could win the lease because of an overbid, in paying the price of the second highest bidder it would pay more than $25,000. It would rather not have won it.

Secondly, would Company 1 ever wish to bid less than $25,000? Again the answer is no. Since the price it will pay if it wins the lease is independent of its bid (it depends only on the amount of the second highest bid), Company 1 cannot save money by underbidding. It may, however, lose the lease by underbidding, when it could have won it at a price under $25,000 by bidding honestly. Thus, either overbidding or underbidding cannot help the company, and may well hurt it. The imperative to honesty is clear, and independent of guesses about other companies' behavior.

With each company bidding its true value, the lease will go to Company 1 at a price of $24,000, an efficient outcome.

At one stroke, Vickrey's scheme solves all three problems we have noted. Companies are motivated to reveal their true preferences, no company has to worry about strategic considerations, and the award which is made is economically efficient. We should also note, as Vickrey did, that this scheme is equivalent to awarding the lease by an open English auction. In such an auction, Company 1 would win the lease when Company 2 drops out of the bidding, which would happen at Company 2's true value of $24,000.

There are two potential problems with implementing this scheme. The first is that the scheme is only usable in situations where it can be safely assumed that each company's goal is only to benefit itself, not to hurt other companies. If Company 2 wished to hurt Company 1 in the example, it might bid an insincere $24,900 with an aim not to win the lease, but to drive up the price which Company 1 must pay. In other words, the companies involved must not be too competitive-minded. The second problem is that the scheme is vulnerable to "bid rigging" by coalitions of companies, but it is no more so than the standard system. Under both systems, there must be provisions to avoid collusion.

It is disappointing that Vickrey's idea was never experimented within many realms in which it might be useful. The only exception I know of is the mail-order auction business, where customers are often asked to mail in their bids on merchandise, with the auctioned item going to the highest bidder at a price of $1 more than the second highest bid [1]. The theoretical promise of Vickrey's idea for the free rider problem in economics and the voting-by-bid problem was likewise to be unfulfilled for a decade.

3.5 A Preference Revealing Process: The Clarke Tax

The correct motivational idea to induce honest revelation of demand for public goods, in other words the theoretical solution to the free rider problem in economics, was developed in preliminary form by E.H. Clarke [4] and more completely by Groves and Ledyard [8]. The application of this idea to voting by bid, which we will consider, was first made by Tideman and Tullock [15].

As before, each voter will be asked to submit monetary bids for the alternatives, and again we can ask, if we wish, that a voter's bids for all alternatives sum to zero. However, we will not collect from each voter the amount he bid for the winning alternative, but instead that amount of his bid which <u>made a difference to the outcome.</u> Consider our example in Section 3.3:

	a	b	c	Result without Voter i			Clarke Tax
Voter 1	-40	15	25	20*	-25	5	15 (=20-5)
Voter 2	20	0	-20	-40	-10	50*	0
Voter 3	-10	25	-15	-10	-35	45*	0
Voter 4	-20	-15	35	0	5*	- 5	10 (=5-(-5))
Voter 5	30	-35	5	-50	25*	25*	0
	-20	-10	+30*				25

(*=winner)

where alternative c won. Consider Voter 1: how did his bids affect the outcome? <u>Without</u> Voter 1 the outcome would have been a: 20, b: -25 and c: 5. Alternative a would have beaten alternative c by $15. We charge Voter 1 a tax, called a <u>Clarke Tax</u>, of $15. Similarly for the other voters. Without Voter 2 the outcome would have been a: -40, b: -10 and c: 50, and c still would have won. Hence Voter 2 did not affect the outcome at all, and is charged no Clarke tax.

The general scheme is this. Suppose that with Voter i an alternative x is selected, but without Voter i another alternative y would have won, beating x by $m. Voter i's Clarke tax is $m. Without Voter 5, for instance, alternative b would have tied c, but since b would not have beaten c, Voter 5's Clarke tax is still 0.

Notice that under this scheme, the voters who favor the winning alternative still pay, but they now pay the amount by which they influenced the decision. One ethical rationale for this payment might be that each voter is paying exactly the amount by which his participation <u>reduced</u> the total utility of other voters. Losers are not compensated. The $25 collected in Clarke taxes represents the cost of decision making.

The justifying virtue of this system is that it motivates sincere revelation of preferences, by the same reasoning that shows Vickrey's scheme does for sealed bids. Consider Voter 1, for instance, asking if it might be wise to overstate the true amount by which he favors, say, alternative c over a (this true amount is $65). This would only be useful if c would not beat a when Voter 1 stated his true difference of $65, but would beat a if he exaggerated his difference. But if this were the case, the amount which his vote would contribute to the selection of c over a would exceed $65, and hence his Clarke tax would exceed $65. If he obtained his preference by overbidding, his Clarke tax would be more than obtaining that preference is worth to him.

Would Voter 1 wish to understate his preference for c over a? The only motivation for doing this would be to try to save money. But if c continues to win, Voter 1's Clarke tax is determined _independently_ of the amount he bids (recall that it depends only on the total amounts that the _other_ voters bid). Hence, he could only save money if his underbidding caused alternative a to beat c, and in that case his savings would be less than the amount of his preference for c over a. Likewise, all voters are motivated to state honestly their preference differences between any two alternatives. Again, notice that this is true independently of what they expect other voters to do.

Our problems are solved. We obtain honest revelation of preferences, no voter has to worry about what other voters will do, and a socially optimal decision using intensities of preferences is made.

As in Section 3.4, for this system to work we must assume, for instance, that voters do not wish to hurt other voters, and that voters do not form coalitions. We must also ask if the system is at all applicable to cases in which voters are not economically and psychologically homogeneous, in other words to cases where it is unreasonable to assume that dollars measure preference intensities in some equitable way. We will consider these problems in the next Section.

3.6 Problems with Implementing the Preference Revealing Process

We will consider problems of four types.
Problem 1.

The Clarke tax _is_ a tax: it may mean collecting money from voters for their participation in the decision making process. It may not be suitable to do this in a given decision-making situation, and there may even be legal barriers to doing it. On the other hand, there may be situations in which it is possible. One requirement which must certainly be met is that the decision which is made must be implemented. We would not use this process in a Policy Advisory Committee, for members would justifiably object to paying for a decision which might be overruled.

One ameliorating fact is that usually not very _much_ money will be collected in Clarke taxes, especially if there are a number of voters involved in the process. Recall that if a voter's bids do not change the outcome, that voter pays no Clarke tax. With a fairly large number of voters, chances are good that _no_ individual voter's bids will change the outcome, so that no Clarke tax at all will be collected. In such a case, the _threat_, if you will, of a Clark tax still operates to ensure honest bidding.

It might be thought that any money collected in Clarke taxes could be refunded to the voters, say to those who placed negative bids on the winning alternative. Unfortu-

nately, this cannot be done wthout destroying the preference revealing incentive of the scheme: if it were done,
voters would have incentive to place insincere negative
bids on the alternative they believed would win. In fact,
the money collected in Clarke taxes should not be used for
any purpose which the voters would consider beneficial to
them. Consider this example:

	a	b	c		Clarke Tax
Voter 1	-40	15	25		55
Voter 2	40	0	-40	(insincere)	0
Voter 3	-10	25	-15		0
Voter 4	-20	-15	35		45
Voter 5	30	-35	5		20
	0	-10	+10*		120

If Voter 2 bid insincerely as above, alternative c would
still win, but now $120 would be collected in Clarke taxes
instead of the $25 in the earlier example. If that money
was used in any way which would benefit Voter 2, she would
have incentive to raise Clarke taxes by bidding insincerely
in this way.   It is perhaps extreme to say that Clarke tax
money must be"wasted," but it should be used to benefit
segments of society which do not include our voters.
      If collecting money from voters is objectionable,
there is one thing we can do. We could give a payment of
$10, to say, to all voters before and independent of the
decision making process. The process itself would then not
be affected, and after Clarke taxes were collected most of
the voters in our example would come out ahead. We could
not know, of course, exactly what payment we should make to
obtain a "balanced budget," since the payment must not depend on the amount to be collected.
Problem 2.
      Individual voters cannot benefit by insincere bidding
under the preference revealing process, but it happens that
coalitions of voters can. Consider Voters 2 and 5 in the
above example, who prefer alternative a to the winning alternative c. Individually, they cannot profitably obtain
alternative a. However, suppose they agree to both bid
insincerely large amounts for alternative a:

Voter	a	b	c		Result without Voter i			Clarke Tax
1	-40	15	25		2020*	-25	-1995	0
2	1020	0	-1020	(insincere)	960*	-10	-950	0
3	-10	25	-15		1990*	-35	-1955	0
4	-20	-15	35		2000*	5	-2005	0
5	1030	-35	-995	(insincere)	950*	25	-975	0
	1980*	-10	-1970					0

(*=winner)

58

Alternative a then wins, and our renegade Voters 2 and 5
pay no Clarke tax at all. What has happened, of course, is
that by both bidding large amounts, Voters 2 and 5 have as-
sured that alternative a will win by a larger margin than
either of their individual bids. Since neither of their
individual bids affect the outcome, no tax is paid.

While such coalitional overbidding might work,it could
be very dangerous if several coalitions tried it at once.
For instance, suppose Voters 1 and 4 tried the same technique to assure a win for c over a, but were a little more
cautious:

Voter	a	b	c		Result without Voter i			Clarke Tax
1	-940	15	925	(insincere)	1120*	-25	-1095	0
2	1020	0	-1020	(insincere)	-840	-10	850*	1690
3	-10	25	-15		190*	-35	-155	0
4	-920	-15	935	(insincere)	1100*	5	-1105	0
5	1030	-35	-995	(insincere)	-850	25	825*	1675
	180*	-10	-170					3365

(*=winner)

Voters 2 and 5 have been caught and punished severely for
their insincerity.

A simple modification which should be effective
against coalitional manipulation would be to put a reasonable ceiling on allowed bids. The ceiling could be high
enough not to interfere with sincere bidding, but its
presence would discourage extreme manipulative attempts.
It would require larger coalitions to manipulate the outcome and increase the danger in such attempts.

Problem 3.

Suppose that our voters are of different economic
circumstances. This is probably the case in most decision
making situations, especially in environmental decision
making, where the parties involved may be citizen organiza-
tions, municipalities and industries as well as individuals. In this case, one can adapt the Clarke tax idea to
weight different voters' bids differently. Suppose, for
instance, that in our example we wished to weight Voter 2's
vote three times as heavily as the others':

Voter	a	b	c		Result without Voter i			Clarke Tax
1	-40	15	25		60*	-25	-35	0
2	3x(20	0	-20)		-40	-10	50*	30=.33(50-(-40))
3	-10	25	-15		30*	-35	5	0
4	-20	-15	35		40*	5	-45	0
5	30	-35	5		-10	25*	-15	35=(25-(-10))
Weighted sum:	+20*	-10	-10					65

(*=winner)

59

We compute the weighted sum to see that alternative a wins. Without Voter 2, alternative c would have beaten alternative a by $90. This would correspond to $30 of Voter 2's bid, weighted thrice. Hence Voter 2's Clarke tax is $30. This method of handling weighting preserves the motivational incentives of the process.

In any particular situation, how we should weight bids will be a delicate and controversial matter. The point is, however, that we can weight votes just as well in this preference revealing process as we can in any other process.

Problem 4.

The preference revealing process should only be used in situations where we otherwise would not know voters' preferences quantitatively. For instance, in the Dorfman-Jacoby example we have used, it is assumed that we actually have cost-benefit figures available for all participants. In such a case we do not need a preference revealing process, and the question of decision making using intensities of preferences boils down to the "weighting" problem. However, even in the Dorfman-Jacoby context there are two factors which might make the preference revealing process useful. The first is that Dorfman and Jacoby quantify benefits of pollution control, in a fairly standard but unconvincing way, as user-days gained at recreational facilities. If we distrust such indirect quantification, we may wish to have people reveal perceived benefits directly using a preference revealing process. Secondly, Dorfman and Jacoby also assume that the cost of pollution control, for instance at the Cannery, is known. In Wisconsin, anyway, it has proved very difficult to obtain reliable pollution control cost figures from industry. Here, again, direct preference revelation may hold the key.

3.7 Conclusions

The question of how to take intensities of preferences into account in collective decision making has traditionally proved to be very difficult. One problem has been the difficulty of measuring intensity of preference in a meaningful way - the problem of defining and measuring cardinal utility. A second fundamental problem is the problem of inter-personal comparison of utility.

The two techniques we have discussed in this Chapter are recent suggestions for dealing with this question. Approval voting gives voters a chance to communicate at least limited information about the relative intensities of their preferences for different alternatives, according to where they draw the line between "approving" and "not approving". One great advantage of approval voting is its simplicity – it is easy to implement, and easily understood by voters. I believe it is the appropriate voting form for a large number of decision making situations.

Voting by bid allows voters to communicate exact information about the relative intensities of their preferences among alternatives, and also to give the absolute intensity of their preferences in terms of the (assumed) universal standard of money. The problem here is one of enforcing honesty. We have seen that collecting the bids for the winning alternative will **not** enforce honesty. The recently discovered preference revealing process of the Clarke tax does enforce honesty and hence represents a major theoretical breakthrough. Whether this theoretical breakthrough can be widely applied in real decision making situations remains to be seen. The objections discussed in Section 6 do not seem insurmountable. The major problem may be the sophistication required of voters: the method would seem to be most applicable to decision making by fairly small groups of intelligent and highly concerned voters. In that context, I believe that the Clarke tax, and the related Vickrey bidding scheme, are exciting ideas with promise for the future.

PROBLEMS

1) The results of approval voting will depend on how many alternatives each voter decides to vote for, i.e. 'approve of.' In the Dorfman-Jacoby example as analyzed on page 49, alternative #11 was the winner. Find which alternative is the winner under the following kinds of voter behaviors:
   a) B votes for its top two choices, P and C vote for their top choice, W for its top three choices.
   b) B, P and C vote for only their top choice, W for its top four choices.
   c) B, P and W vote for only their top choice, C for its top three choices.
   d) B votes for its top four choices, P and C only for their top choice, W for its top three choices.

2) The results of exercise 1 raise possibilities of strategic behavior on the part of voters, where each voter may wish to consider what the other voters will do. Suppose that it is known that C and P will vote only for their top choice, and voters believe that B is planning to vote for 8, 9 and W is planning to vote for 11, 9, 13, 8.
   a) What will be the outcome if voters follow these strategies?
   b) Show that B would be tempted to vote for only 8.

c) Show that W would be tempted to vote for only 11, 9, 13.

d) If both B and W yield to temptation, what will the outcome be?

e) Assume that in the event of a tie vote, the eventual winner will be selected at random from among those alternatives with the highest vote total. Use the cardinal utilities as given on page 50 to show that B and W would both be <u>worse</u> off if they both yield to temptation, while C and P would both be better off.

3) Verify that Borda count and the Black and Copeland methods would all produce a three-way tie in the example on page 51.

4) Suppose that four voters' honest bids for three alternatives are

	a	b	c
Voter 1	35	-10	-25
Voter 2	0	20	-20
Voter 3	-25	15	10
Voter 4	-10	-15	25

Find which alternative wins and calculate the Clarke tax paid by each voter.

5) Suppose that Voter 1, who prefers a to b, decides to ensure the selection of alternative a by submitting dishonest bids of 135, -60, -75. Verify that this dishonesty does produce a win for a. Calculate the Clarke tax Voter 1 will pay. Is it worth this much to Voter 1 to have a instead of b?

6) In fact, both voters 1 and 4 prefer a to b. Show how they might agree to bid dishonestly to obtain alternative a without paying any Clarke tax, assuming that voters 2 and 3 bid honestly.

BIBLIOGRAPHIC NOTES

The subject of cardinal utilities has a vast literature, to which one fairly recent guide is [7].

Approval voting is a subject of current interest to political scientists. Properties of approval voting are analyzed in [2], [3], [11] and [18]. A proposal to use approval voting in Presidential primaries can be found in [10]. For a recent discussion of approval voting compared to various voting systems in Chapter Two, see Samuel Merrill, "Decision Analysis for Multicandidate Voting Systems," UMAP Module #384.

The voting by bid scheme of Section 3.3 has recently been analyzed mathematically in [6].

Preference revealing (or 'demand revealing' or 'incentive compatible') processes are the subject of active current research. The special issue of <u>Public Choice</u> [14] contains thirteen papers on the subject, some of them addressing specifically questions of implementability. It also has a good historical introduction by Tideman and a bibliography. Downing and Tideman in [5] attempt to apply a demand revealing process specifically to pollution control problems. A discussion of the Clarke tax and some other interesting proposals is in [13].

REFERENCES

1. Americana Mail Auction, 4015 Kilmer Avenue, Allentown, Pa. 18104, 1976.

2. S. J. Brams, "One man, N votes" Mathematical Association of America Modules in Applied Mathematics, 334 Upson Hall, Cornell University, Ithaca, N.Y. 14853, 1976.

3. S. J. Brams, and P. Fishburn, "Approval voting", <u>American Political Science Review</u> 72 (1978) 831-847.

4. E. H. Clarke, "Multipart pricing of public goods", <u>Public Choice</u> 11 (1971) 17-33.

5. P. B. Downing and T. N. Tideman, "Efficiency in pollution control institutions," Center for Study of Public Choice, VPI&SU, Blacksburg, Va. 24061, 1976.

6. L. Dubins, "Group decision devices," <u>American Mathematical Monthly</u> 84 (1977) 350-56.

7. P. Fishburn, <u>Utility Theory for Decision Making</u>, John Wiley, New York, 1970.

8. T. Groves and J. Ledyard, "Optimal allocation of public goods: a solution to the 'free rider problem'," <u>Econometrica</u> 45 (1977) 783-810.

9. R. A. Joslyn, "Impact of decision rules in multicandidate campaigns: the case of the 1972 Democratic Presidential nomination", <u>Public Choice</u> 25 (1976) 1-18.

10. J. Kellet and K. Mott, "Presidential primaries: measuring popular choice," <u>Polity</u> 9 (1977) 528-37.

11. S. Merrill, "Approval voting: a 'best buy' method for multi-candidate elections?" <u>Mathematics Magazine</u> 52 (1979) 98-102.

12. M. Metfessel, "A proposal for quantitative reporting of comparative judgments" <u>Journal of Psychology</u>, 24 (1947) 229-235.

13. D. Mueller, <u>Public Choice</u>, Cambridge University Press, 1979. (Note that this is a book, not the periodical).

14. T. N. Tideman, ed., Special supplement to volume 29 of <u>Public Choice</u>, on demand revealing processes, Spring 1977.

15. T. N. Tideman, and G. Tullock, "A new and superior process for making social choices," <u>Journal of Political Economy</u> 84 (1976) 1145-59.

16. W. Vickrey, "Counterspeculation, auctions and competitive sealed tenders," <u>Journal of Finance</u> 16 (1961) 8-37.

17. J. von Neumann and O. Morgenstern, <u>The Theory of Games and Economic Behavior</u>, Princeton University Press, 1953 (first published 1944).

18. R. J. Weber, "Comparison of voting systems," Cowles Foundation Discussion Paper No. 498, Cowles Foundation, Yale University, 1978.

Chapter One

1) a) 3211   2311   2131   2113
       3121   1321   1231   1213
       3112   1312   1132   1123

3) a) AB,AC,BC   [2;1,1,1]   (1/3,1/3,1/3,0)
   b) AB,AC,AD,BCD   [3;2,1,1,1]   (1/2,1/6,1/6,1/6)
   c) AB,AC,BCD   [5;3,2,2,1]   (5/12,3/12,3/12,1/12)
   d) AB,ACD,BCD   [4;2,2,1,1]   (1/3,1/3,1/6,1/6)
   The moral here is that seemingly small changes can make
   large changes in power.

4) No, by examining Table 1.1.

5) 31111   13111   11311   11131   11113

6) a) 10/16   b) 10/16   c) 9/16   d) 7/16

8) a) E.g. for [6;4,4,1,1,1]:
          44111   41411   41141   41114   14411
          14141   14114   11441   11414   11144
      The 4's pivot 6/10 of the time, so each 4 has 3/10 or
      30% of the power.

9)
   Power of 11-bloc $= \dfrac{T_7 + T_6 - T_{-4} - T_{-5}}{2T_{16}}$

   $= \dfrac{28 + 21 - 0 - 0}{272}$

   $= .180$

   which is lower than 11/40 = .275.

   Power of 14-bloc $= \dfrac{T_{10} + T_9 - T_{-4} - T_{-5}}{2T_{16}}$

   $= \dfrac{55 + 45 - 0 - 0}{272}$

   $= .368$

   which is slightly higher than 14/40 = .350.

10)

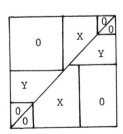

11) AAABB   AABAB   AABBA   ABAAB   ABABA
     ABBAA   BAAAB   BAABA   BABAA   BBAAA

     The A's pivot 8/10 of the time, so each A has 8/30 of
     the power. The B's pivot 2/10 of the time, so each B
     has 1/10 of the power.

12) 15.03, 10.67

15) An A pivots if the middle B precedes the middle A, and
     a B pivots if the middle A precedes the middle B. If
     one of these conditions holds for a given ordering, the
     other condition holds for the reversed ordering (i.e.
     the original ordering read backwards). Hence the or-
     derings pair off, and there are exactly as many
     orderings in which an A pivots as orderings in which a
     B pivots.

16) There are $\binom{8}{3}$ = 56 orderings. An A pivots if it is
     preceded by one other A and 4 or 5 B's. This happens
     in 16 ways. The power of an A is 2/21, and the power
     of a B is 3/21, for a ratio of 2:3.

17) There are 504 orderings. P pivots in 192, an S in 162,
     an H in 150. The power indices are P: .381   S: .107
     H: .060

Chapter Two

1)   If every voter prefers x to y, y will never be in first
     place, and will get zero plurality votes.

2)   The only possible effect of a change of preference in
     favor of x would be to possibly increase x's plurality
     vote and lower that of some other candidate (this would
     happen if the change moved x into first place).

3)   Yes.

4)   For the Condorcet loser criterion, note that if y loses
     all pairwise contests, then it is ranked below each
     other alternative more than it is ranked above it, so
     that it must have **below average** Borda count, and cannot
     have the highest Borda count.

6)   Pareto: If all voters rank x higher than y, then x
     beats y in a pairwise contest, so if there is a
     Condorcet winner, it cannot be y. If there is no
     Condorcet winner, x has a higher Borda count than y, so
     y can't be the Borda winner either.
     Monotonicity: Moving x up in some preference orderings
     can't cause it to lose pairwise contests it won before,
     so if it was a Condorcet winner, it still is. If there

wasn't a Condorcet winner and x was the Borda winner, moving x up can't make any other alternative a Condorcet winner, and can only increase x's Borda count while possibly lowering those of other alternatives.

7) Pareto: If x always ranks higher than y, then x beats y in pairwise contest and whenever y beats z, x also beats z. Thus x has a higher Copeland score than y. Smith: Every alternative in A beats more alternatives than every alternative in B, and loses to fewer, so has a higher Copeland score.

9) Sequential: 8 or 9 or 11 or 13 or 9-13
   Plurality: 8
   Runoff: 8
   Hare: 8
   Coombs: 8
   Borda: 13
   Black: 13
   Nanson: 13
   Copeland: 8

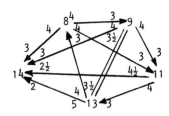

The possible sequential outcome of 13 would be worse for B than the tie between 11 and 13 when B had only two votes. Same for the Nanson outcome.

10)

	[5;4,2,2,1]	[5;3,2,2,1]	[4;2,2,1,1]	[3;1,1,1,1]
Sequential	a,b,c,d	a,b,d,cd	a,b,d,cd	a,b,d,cd
Plurality	a	a	ad	abcd
Runoff	d	d	d	abcd
Hare	d	d	d	abcd
Coombs	a	a	d	d
Borda	a	a	a	ad
Black	a	a	a	ad
Nanson	a	d	d	d
Copeland	ab	ab	ad	ad

12) Sequential: Example 1 with order b-a-c-d. Eliminate c.
    Plurality: Example 2, eliminate b
    Runoff and Hare: Example 4, eliminate b
    Coombs: Example 5, eliminate b
    Borda: Example 7, eliminate c
    Black: Example 8, eliminate w, then z
    Nanson: Example 10, eliminate b
    Copeland: Example 1, eliminate c

13) a) The Pareto and monotonicity criteria are satisfied because the rule depends entirely on the results of pairwise contests. For Smith, note that nothing in B can beat anything in A in one or two (or any number of) steps.
    b) abc.

Chapter Three

1) a) Vote totals are (2,3,1,2,2) and alternative #9 wins. (Remember B and P have two votes each, while C and W have only one.)
   b) (3,1,1,2,2) #8 wins
   c) (2,0,2,1,3) #14 wins
   d) (2,3,3,4,2) #13 wins!

2) a) (3,3,1,2,2) #8 and #9 would tie.
   b) If B voted for only #8, the result would be (3,1,1, 2,2) and #8 would win. B would prefer this to the tie between #8 and #9.
   c) The result would be (2,3,1,2,2) with #9 winning, which W would prefer to the tie.
   d) The result would be (2,1,1,2,2), a tie among 8,13, 14.
   e) Under the given assumption about tie-breaking, B and W would prefer 8-9 to 8-13-14, while P and C would prefer 8-13-14 to 8-9.

3) The Borda count would give 5,5,5. Since in pairwise contests b beats a, a beats c, and c beats b, there is no Condorcet winner and Black's method reduces to a Borda count. Copeland gives 1-1=0 for all three alternatives.

4)

				Result without			
Voter	a	b	c	voter i			Clarke Tax
1	35	-10	-25	-35	20*	15	0
2	0	20	-20	0	-10	10*	10-(-10)=20
3	-25	15	10	25*	-5	-20	25-(-5)=30
4	-10	-15	25	10	25*	-35	0
	0	10*	-10				

5)

			Result without			
a	b	c	voter i			Clarke Tax
135	-60	-75	-35	20*	15	20-(35)=55
0	20	-20	100*	-60	-40	0
-25	15	10	125*	-55	-70	0
-10	-15	25	110*	-25	-85	0
100*	-40	-60				

The 55 Voter 1 pays in Clarke tax is larger than the 35-(-10)=45 it is worth to him to have a instead of b. We know that this kind of dishonesty can never pay.

6)

a	b	c	Result without voter i			Clarke Tax
135	-60	-75	65*	-30	-35	0
0	20	-20	200*	-110	-90	0
-25	15	10	225*	-105	-120	0
90	-65	-25	110*	-25	-85	0
200*	-90	-110				

This is one among many possibilities. Voters 1 and 4
must simply inflate their bids for a enough so that
either bid by itself would be enough to put a over the
top.